D1231051

# One Family's Forest

Alan Haney ✦ Lowell Klessig

Illustrations by George Gard and Lora Hagen

Back Forty Press

Custer, Wisconsin

Supported by a grant from Wisconsin Environmental Education Board 2009-2010

ISBN: 978-093698417-9
Back Forty Press •1990 Star-B Hill Lane • Custer WI 54423

# Table of Contents

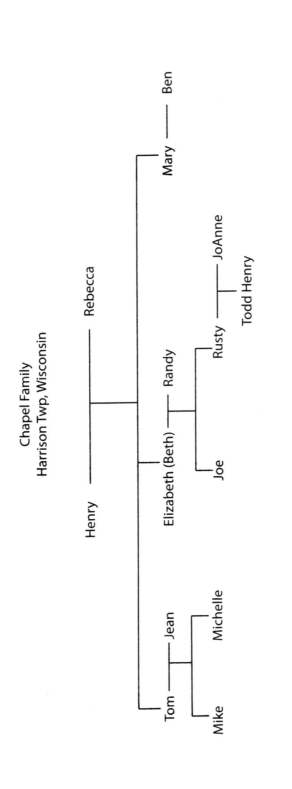

Chapel Family
Harrison Twp, Wisconsin

Henry — Rebecca — Mary — Ben

Tom — Jean

Mike

Michelle

Elizabeth (Beth) — Randy

Joe

Rusty — JoAnne

Todd Henry

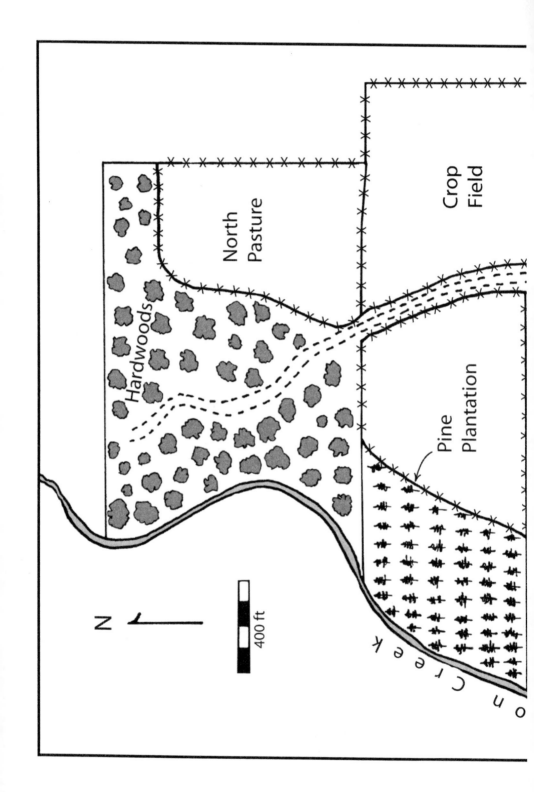

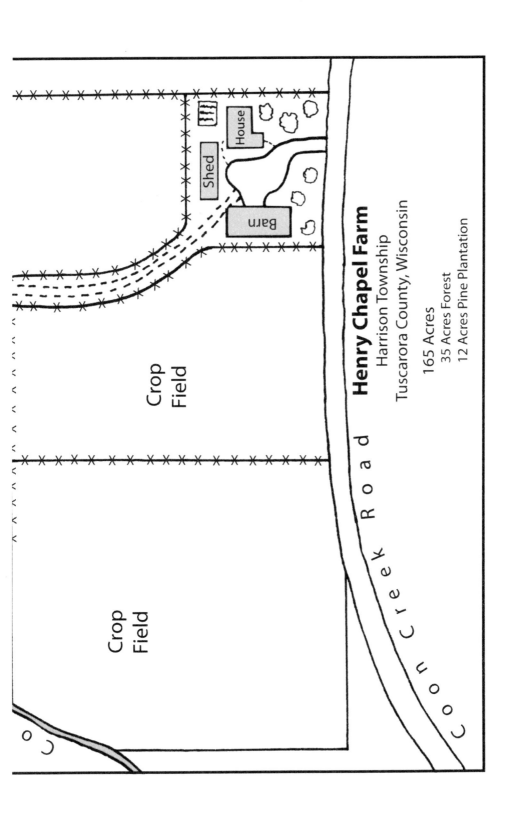

**Henry Chapel Farm**

Harrison Township
Tuscarora County, Wisconsin

165 Acres
35 Acres Forest
12 Acres Pine Plantation

Shed

House

Barn

Crop
Field

Crop
Field

Coon Creek Road

# Acknowledgments

The inspiration for this book was Clyde Samsel's. Ten years ago, Clyde received a copy of a beautiful book prepared by the Swedish government to encourage better management of family forests there. Clyde thought a similar book should be available for this region and was persistent in urging us to write it.

Throughout the preparation of this book, Lora Hagen provided consistent encouragement and editorial suggestions. Because she and her father are woodland owners representative of those for whom the book is prepared, and because she is a talented editor and artist, but not a forester, her input was especially valuable.

Others who offered important feedback and suggestions include Clyde Samsel and Gerry Mich, Wisconsin Family Forests; John Duplissis, UW-Extension Forester; Paul Pingrey, Genny Fannucchi, and Carol Nielson, Wisconsin Department of Natural Resources; Bill Horvath, Wisconsin Woodland Owners Association; and Katie Rojas-Jahn and Gigi La Budde, Community Forestry Resource Center.

Photos were provided by Lowell Klessig, Laura Pflibsen, and Lora Hagen.

While the book would never have been completed without the help and encouragement of those mentioned above and others, any errors of fact or omission are the sole responsibility of the authors.

# Foreword

*One Family's Forest* is a story about people and place, about a family and the land that sustained them, land they deeply loved. It is a story of challenges and how the challenges were overcome as they strived to keep the family farm they all cherished intact for future generations. It is a story that can help every landowner keep their land intact and maintain the health and productivity of the land for the long haul.

The authors bring decades of academic and practical experience to this non-technical how-to guide that can help farmers and forest land owners plan for the future. *One Family's Forest* is about a family's relationship with the land, and the methods they applied to sustain the health and productivity of farm and forest. This book turns the concept of "sustainability" into actual practice for the everyday landowner. It brings conservation to reality on the land.

Aldo Leopold, a preeminent conservationist and professor at the University of Wisconsin, wrote of the need for a "land ethic." Leopold succinctly defined the ethic as follows:

> *"The practice of conservation must spring from a conviction of what is ethically right and aesthetically right, as well as what is economically expedient. A thing is right only when it tends to preserve the integrity, stability and beauty of the community, and the community includes soil, waters, fauna, and flora, as well as people."*

Each generation faces new challenges, needs and desires in this rapidly changing society. *One Family's Forest* is about the conviction to keep the family farm intact and in the family. While it is impossible for any human not to have at least a minimal impact on the land, there is an associated obligation, as was eloquently stated by Aldo Leopold more that a half-century ago:

> *"We end, at what might be called the standard paradox of the*

*twentieth century: our tools are better than we are, and grow bet-
ter and faster than we do. They suffice to crack the atom, to com-
mand the tides.  But they do not suffice for the oldest task in human history: to live on a piece of land without spoiling it."*

—Aldo Leopold (1938)

*One Family's Forest* is a valuable guide that can help each of us to live on
the land "without spoiling it."

Michael Dombeck

October, 2010

Stevens Point, Wisconsin

# Preface

*One Family's Forest* tells the story of Henry and Rebecca Chapel and their extended family, struggling to keep their farm intact across three generations. The story relates how they discover that their forest can provide more than a pleasant place to walk or hunt, and how they work through the challenges of continuing the farm intact from one generation to the next. We have avoided interrupting the story by presenting the more technical aspects of forest management in appendices, introduced through brief sidebars in the text.

As with trees, creative projects begin with a seed. In this case, the seed was an idea planted by Clyde Samsel. In October 2006, with sponsorship from the Wisconsin Environmental Education Board, a workshop was held to address the question of what resources were most needed to support community forestry in Wisconsin. Representatives at the Workshop included UW-Extension, Wisconsin Department of Natural Resources, Wisconsin Woodland Owners Association, Community Forestry Resource Center, Dovetail Partners, Wisconsin Family Forests, University of Wisconsin, and private woodland owners. The opinion of those participating in the Workshop was that the most-needed resource was a non-technical book that explained the basic principles of forest management.

After considering and dismissing many ways such a book might be organized, the authors decided on a novel (pun intended) approach. The concept of "community forestry" builds on the idea that neighbors most easily and comfortably learn from one another. As one family gains experience, sharing that knowledge enriches their neighbors and facilitates community relationships. Family forest organizations across the country have proven that this approach encourages forest management and community networks. This book explores that process through a fictional but conceptually accurate story.

There is great variation in both the forests and the cultures within the United States. While we would like to think that Henry's and Rebecca's story would be of interest to woodland owners anywhere, the setting of their forest and related management issues is Wisconsin. Therefore, the information one can glean from this book will be most useful to forest owners in the Upper Midwest or New England. Examples, practices, and policies are primarily drawn from Wisconsin, although similar resources and policies apply elsewhere. With  an Internet connection on  your computer, you can quickly find comparable information for your state. Contact your county Extension Service, public library, or natural resource representative to get started. This book will guide you to the kinds of information you need and the questions you should ask.

# Chapter 1
# Uncertain Future

Slowly, Henry worked his way up the hill from the creek where a few large hemlocks shaded pools of clear water. It was a warm day for early April, and he could feel the temperature rise as he climbed. He remembered seeing the creek for the first time 47 years earlier when he and Rebecca were looking to buy the farm. They hadn't paid much attention to the woods, being more concerned about the fields, barn, and house where they hoped to make a living and a raise a family. He was 27 then, Rebecca was 25, and they were full of energy and hope.

"The farm has been good to us," Henry thought. "We've raised three wonderful children. Not so wonderful when Tom totaled the family car his senior year in high school, but that was a long time ago," Henry mused with a wry smile. Tom now farms with his dad. Tom's son, Mike, nearly 20, also helps with the harvesting and major projects when on break from college. Tom and his wife Jean also have a daughter, Michelle, who hopes to study pre-med when she begins college in the fall.

A turkey gobbled from near the top of the ridge. Henry, breathing deeply from the climb, stopped to listen. When he and Rebecca first moved to the farm, there were no turkeys. Although they had become common since reintroduction began in 1970s, Henry still got a thrill out of seeing or hearing them. He didn't hunt turkeys, but Tom and Mike did, and often bagged a tom. The mix of hardwood forests and open farm fields are ideal turkey habitat.

Another gobble, this time from farther down the ridge. Henry knew the tom was on the prowl for a hen. The tom was heading south, toward the hayfield that Henry and Tom planned to disk for corn in a few weeks. On nice mornings the hens often sunned in the field along the south side of the woods, and foraged in the grass for insects and seeds. Near the top of the ridge, Henry sat down with his back against a large white oak. Around him were white and red oaks, red maple, black cherry, and a few white pines. White ash, sugar maple, basswood, and several ironwoods were scattered lower on the slope along with the few big hemlocks that Henry especially loved. There were even a couple of bitternut hickories near the creek and Henry knew where one butternut grew near the north property line. The 38-acre forest had never been cut since Henry owned the land, partly because the slope from the ridge to the creek was steep, but mostly because Henry liked the woods and worried that logging would destroy it. It was here, on the west slope, that he could find

the first hepatica blooming in the spring, and near the ridge trailing arbutus crept among the roots of old oaks. He and Rebecca used to walk here, hand in hand, listening to the great-horned owls in winter, or chorus frogs in spring, and later in the summer watching for the first fireflies. Soon, he thought, we've got to decide how to deed this property to the kids. He and Rebecca had lain awake many nights discussing how they might keep the farm intact, yet be fair to all three children .

In addition to Tom and his family, Henry and Rebecca's other two children, Elizabeth and Mary, are both married. Beth, as they called Elizabeth, lives near Chicago. She and her husband Randy have two boys, both in their early teens. Mary and her husband, Ben, run a bookstore in town. They have no children.

Henry and Rebecca had paid off the mortgage ten years ago, but they had not been able to save much money since. With hard work and careful management, they had made enough to maintain the barns and remodel the house, and help their daughters through college. Henry had never gotten beyond 8th grade, having to work full-time when his father died, but he and Rebecca valued education and were determined that their children would be well educated. Tom was anxious to start farming right out of high school, so didn't want to continue his education. Although he didn't have a college degree, Tom took advantage of short courses and information he could glean from publications and Extension specialists.

Henry and Tom used soil-conserving farming practices that sustained good yields. But milk prices were often at or sometimes below break-even, and were it not for Rebecca's garden and the chickens, it might have been tough keeping the farm intact. Henry and Rebecca couldn't stand the thought of having to divide the farm, or worse, selling it to someone who would break it up for development. "Why, these very woods would make an outstanding place for several fancy houses," Henry thought with considerable discomfort.

Ideally, Tom might buy out his sisters' interest, but Henry knew that wasn't possible. Tom and Jean saved enough to help Mike with his college expenses, and they hoped to help their daughter, Michelle, with her schooling. Because the value of land had increased so much, especially in the last 20 years, Tom could never afford to buy out his sisters, Mary and Beth. And it wouldn't be fair to just deed the farm to Tom, Henry thought, although Tom and his son had done most of the work to keep the place going the last ten years. Henry knew that if Jean hadn't had her teaching job with health benefits, Tom would have had to find work off the farm.

Although he hated to think about it, Henry looked at the big trees around him, realizing that they represented capital that could be converted to cash. "Wonder what they'd bring," he pondered. "There's also the 12 acres of pines Rebecca and me planted that second spring we were on the farm," he recalled. "Maybe there's some value there."

With some effort, Henry stood. He pulled a red bandana from the pocket of his old, but clean coveralls and wiped sweat from his smoothly shaven face. Wrinkles around his eyes reflected his tendency to smile and suggested his good nature, a characteristic that Tom also exhibited. Beth also was easy going, like her dad, but Mary was more intense, and tended to worry too much, Henry thought.

Reaching the old woods road on the ridge, he turned toward the house. After lunch with Tom and Rebecca, Henry planned to replace some of the damaged boards on the south door of the barn until it was time to start the evening milking. Although Tom could milk the 56 cows in less than two hours, Henry liked to help as much as he could, to relieve Jean. Jean could then help Michelle and Rebecca with supper, when her daughter wasn't busy with some after-school activity. Even though Tom and Jean lived across the road, the five of them often eat together. There were six at the table when Mike was home. Michelle and Rebecca now shared responsibility for the chickens. Mike had a knack for mechanics, and since grade school liked tinkering with the farm equipment. Maintenance of his 1995 Corolla got highest priority, however.

That night at dinner, Henry shared some of his thoughts with the others. "You know, Rebecca and me aren't going to be around here for many more years," he started. Tom hesitated in his eating, shooting a concerned look at his dad, but didn't interrupt. "I was thinking this morning," Henry continued, "that maybe we should get someone to help us figure out how much the timber on the ridge and pine plantation might be worth."

"Dad, you know how much you love those big trees on the ridge," Tom said. "Why would you consider selling them?"

"Well, I wasn't thinking of selling them myself, but I thought maybe you could use the money to buy out your sisters' interest in the farm," Henry replied. "As much as I'd hate to see any of those trees cut, I'd hate worse to see the farm broken up or sold."

Henry took a bite, chewed slowly, swallowed, then continued when no one else spoke. "Your mom and me have pondered on this some," he said, "and we would like to see you continue with the farm. We particularly would hate to see it sold to someone who didn't appreciate it the way we do."

"Lord knows it's no easy way to make a living," Rebecca added, looking at Tom, "but farming's been a good life for us and we know the place means a lot to you and Jean. We assume you'd like to continue working the place if we can find a way that's fair to everyone."

"Yes, of course we would," Tom replied. "But I don't see how we can buy out Mary and Beth. Those trees aren't worth that much, are they?"

"I don't know," Henry said, "but I think I'll call the local Natural Resources office in the morning and see if they can tell me how to find out."

# Chapter 2
# A Walk in the Woods

The next morning after chores, Henry opened the phone book to find a natural resources number. It turned out to be quite confusing. The phone book referred him to the blue pages for government offices. He couldn't find anything for forestry under county government. So he tried the state government listings. There he located "Natural Resources, Dept Of" and called the DNR Customer Service number. He got a long recorded message with a lengthy menu of options. One option referred him to a forester, but when he pressed the number, he got another recording saying that the forester was not available, but please leave a message and number. He left a brief message indicating what he wanted.

When he came in for lunch, Rebecca told him a government forester had called back telling him that he should contact a consulting forester, or to call back if he had questions about how to locate one.

Henry had lots of questions. He didn't know how to find a consulting forester he could trust. There were five listed in the Yellow Pages, but he noticed that three were associated with sawmills and another was with a paper company. He figured they might be more interested in buying his timber cheaply than in helping him. He couldn't find out anything about the fifth consulting forester listed, but he appeared to be associated with some kind of management service. Henry didn't think he was in the market for management services; he just wanted to know what his trees were worth and whether some could be harvested without wrecking his woods.

Henry called the Natural Resources Service Center back and got through to the regional forester. The regional forester said the forester in his county could walk through his woods and give him a ballpark estimate of what was there and its worth, depending on how he might want it harvested. Henry was also promised a list of consulting foresters who had been trained and certified, and had signed a statement committing them to ethical practices. Henry called the number for the local DNR office and spoke to the forester, hiding his surprise that it was a woman. They made an appointment for her to walk through his woods in three weeks.

Tom was anxious to have someone advise his dad on managing the woods. He had spent several evenings and one rainy Sunday reading about forest management. He was sure there were some things they should be doing to keep the forest healthy, but that always took a lower priority than farm chores which never seemed to be caught up.

Henry and Tom had just finished breakfast when the county forester arrived. She was a young woman, about 30, Henry thought. She was dressed in clean field pants and shirt and wore an orange vest. He noticed that her boots had seen plenty of ware. Tom decided the corn could wait a few hours, and said he'd like to go with them to inspect the woods. Henry explained how important the woods were to him, and wanted her advice about management, harvesting, and estimated cash values. They decided to visit the red pine plantation first.

The plantation trees had been planted in rows spaced eight feet apart, and about eight feet between trees in each row. Because Henry had mowed the weeds for three years after planting, most trees had survived. The forester explained that because the trees had not been thinned, they were spindly. She stressed to Henry and Tom the urgency of thinning, but suggested that only a third of the trees should be removed at this time to avoid others breaking over. Keeping the trees at the proper density, she said, allowed them room to grow but a bit of crowding helped them support one another and they would be straighter trees. She recommended a row thinning, where every third row would be taken out. This could most easily be done, using a mechanical harvester, and bring the best price. That meant about 225 trees per acre could be cut, she explained, totaling about six cords, for a total yield of 120 cords. Remaining pines, she said, would grow better and yield much

---

## QUESTIONS LANDOWNERS SHOULD ASK THEMSELVES BEFORE TALKING WITH A PROFESSIONAL FORESTER

1. What is my favorite spot on my land? Why? How about other members of the family?

2. What are the most important benefits we get from our woods? Some examples are: recreation (hunting, hiking, skiing, bird-watching, photography, etc.), firewood, maple syrup, timber for personal use or sale, pulpwood for sale, or satisfaction just knowing the woods are there.

3. What priority does my family place on the above benefits, i.e., how would you rank them? Do all members of the family agree?

4. Is property tax relief on my woodland acres important?

5. If there were a way to significantly enhance the benefits we get from our woods, would we be interested in learning more about what might be involved?

6. Is our immediate community more attractive to us because of wooded acreage on our property and our neighbors' property? If so, would we be interested in networking with our neighbors to encourage protection of woodlands in our neighborhood?

For questions to ask a professional forester, see Appendix 1.

---

more when next thinned in about 10 years.

They skirted the hay field and entered the woods above the creek. Henry explained that he didn't want the big hemlocks or the old oaks that had survived since before settlement cut, and he also wanted to protect the stream from any disturbance. He also didn't want to "slick off" the woods, but only harvest some of the mature trees to provide room for others to grow. They walked slowly across the woods and back several times. The forester stopped frequently to hold a piece of glass at arm's length. She slowly rotated around the glass through which she appeared to be looking at individual trees. "What are you doing with that piece of glass?" Henry asked.

"This is a prism," she replied. "With it I can estimate the stocking level of the forest."

"What's stocking level?" Tom asked.

"It is the volume of trees per acre, The prism allows me to count trees proportional to their size. Big trees are counted more than little trees. The whole thing works out such that I can estimate the volume of trees per acre."

She said this was an estimate of the "stocking level," sort of like estimating how many cows could be kept on a particular pasture. Too many trees, like too many cows, and they wouldn't grow as well, and would be less likely to remain healthy. The forester also measured the diameter of many trees. As she made notes, they talked about the trees and the woods.

"How do you know what stocking level is appropriate?" Henry wanted to know. "It depends on the site capability," she explained, just as your pasture does. "We pay attention to the mix of species present in the woods, including the herbaceous plants on the forest floor, to guide us. Sites are roughly classified into what we call habitat types accordingly, and studies have been made of optimal stocking levels for each. This is a dry-mesic forest with good to very good potential for mixed northern hardwoods or aspen."

The forester went on to explain that the emerald ash borer was moving across the country and suggested that might be a reason to cut the merchantable ash before they were killed. She asked their opinion on cutting several trees which she said were mature, but would continue to grow slowly for many more years.

We like to have big trees in the forest and don't want to have just a forest of fast-growing young trees," Tom said.

"The decision is yours," the forester responded. "I'm asking only to get an idea of how you want to manage your woods. You have many options." She pointed out that the forest could be clear-cut, with all trees removed. Red maples and oaks would re-sprout and grow back.

If aspen were present, they would re-sprout from roots and might become dominant for many years after a clear-cut," she warned, "but you have few aspen in this stand and you clearly want to maintain a mix of species and sizes. A clear-cut here would encourage more red maple and black cherry, and allow at least some of the oaks to come back from sprouts, but you will be happier with a selection harvest that will maintain more of the larger, old trees."

---

## Plantation Management

There is no easier way to reforest cleared land than to plant it with trees of an appropriate species. As with all forestry practices, the choice of species largely depends on your priorities and the potential of the site. Your local Extension or natural resource office will likely have several bulletins on tree planting and plantation management, or you probably can download bulletins from the Internet. With careful planning and establishment, conifer plantations require little management. Hardwoods are harder to plant and require more follow-up management. Benefits from plantations include income from marginal land, wildlife cover, watershed protection, windbreak, and aesthetics. Studies have shown that conifer plantations interspersed with agricultural fields increases property values. A benefit for some is simply the pleasure of working with trees and spending more time outdoors. (See Appendices 2 and 3.)

---

"You can selectively remove some of the less desirable trees...those that are of poor form or are diseased, or trees likely to get attacked by insects, like the ash borer...along with some of the larger trees," she continued. "That will not greatly alter the appearance of the forest, once the slash has rotted down." She went on to explain that they could speed up the aesthetic recovery of the forest by removing as much slash as possible for pulpwood and firewood.

"We'd like to get a rough estimate of both alternatives," Henry said, although he knew in his heart he could not bring himself to clear-cut the woods.

"Doesn't removing all that wood take a lot of nutrients out of the forest?" Tom asked, thinking of how they had to add fertilizer to their fields to maintain good yields.

"Surprisingly, that's not a problem with this kind of forest," the forester replied. "Most of the nutrients are in leaves, small branches and fruits, along with roots, and those are left in the woods. Also, you don't take off all or most of the plant growth each year like you do in your crop fields. This gives the forest ecosystem time to replenish much of what is lost."

"What about turkeys and deer?" Tom wanted to know. "How would the two alternatives affect them?"

"Deer are a problem," the forester replied. "Clear-cutting favors them because it creates more sprout growth that deer use, especially in late winter. By selectively browsing some species, oaks for example, they encourage red maple or cherry. Turkeys, on the other hand, like the older oaks because they like the acorns and use the bigger trees for roosting."

After an hour they returned to the barnyard where the forester said she needed a few minutes to make notes. Henry and Tom continued discussing how they felt about harvesting the trees.

"I really hate to do it," Henry said, "but if we can harvest without ruining the woods, the money might help us treat the kids evenly. Anyway, the forester suggested that some harvesting would actually make the woods healthy by giving more room to the trees we most want up there"

"It's really up to you, Dad. I know how you feel about the woods. I'll go along with your decision. If we have to give up the farm, we lose the woods anyway. I'm for doing what we have to do to keep the farm, but protect the potential of the forest."

"What do you mean?" Henry asked.

"Well, from what I learned on the Internet," Tom replied, "we could clear-cut the woods if we had to, and in time, it would come back. The potential is still there. The one thing I think we couldn't do would be to damage the woods so that it would never come back as beautiful as it is now."

"I only partially agree," Henry said. "If it were clear-cut, it will never be as beautiful in my lifetime or yours, or even Mike's or Michelle's lifetime. I understand what you mean by the potential...given decades or centuries, the woods might recover to look similar as now. Ideally, my hope is that we could harvest enough wood to help give Mary and Beth a decent inheritance, and keep the woods intact. Of course we'll need to discuss all this with Mary and Beth when we have some more information."

The forester came over to where Henry and Tom were sitting on the porch. "The pine plantation is pretty straightforward," she said. "It wouldn't make sense to clear-cut it at this time, but it needs to be thinned. The plantation will be more productive afterwards, and within three or four years, you won't notice much disturbance down there. You will want to schedule a follow-up thinning in about ten years, and it should bring quite a bit more than this one."

"We agree that we should thin the pines," Henry said.

"You have some very nice hardwoods along the ridge. Many of the trees are over-mature and are losing value," the forester continued.

"How do they lose value?" Tom wanted to know. He remembered

that some of the articles he had read distinguished between economic value, wildlife value, natural beauty value, soil and water conservation value, and something called biodiversity value.

"I'm talking only about economic value," the forester replied. "Some of the trees are old, limbs die, decay sets in, they become hollow," she said. "They don't grow much once they get that old."

"Well, the squirrels don't think they are losing value, and I enjoy looking at them" Henry observed, "but I follow you."

"The good news," the forester said, is that leaving the most desirable trees, what we'd call a timber stand improvement, or tsi (pronounced "tee-ess-eye") harvest will provide some income now, and leave the forest in a healthier condition. There would be some aesthetic loss for several years. Timber harvests, even done well, can be hard to swallow for people like you who love their woods. But in a few years, your woods will look much the same, and trees will grow better and be healthier. You'll also be able to harvest repeatedly with income from timber sales to supplement farm income."

"There are two other options," the forester went on. "Both are what we call regeneration harvests. They involve removing most or all of the trees. One would leave only scattered big trees to provide seeds and limited shade. Some think this favors oaks over red maple. The other is the clear-cut we discussed. If you decided to cut most of the trees, you could essentially triple the amount you could get at this time. I think you could go any of the three ways, but I wouldn't recommend something in between. Either go with the tsi harvest, or a regeneration harvest. Any questions?"

"Yes," asked Henry. "If we cut it lightly now, how soon might we harvest again?"

"Excellent question. The good thing about proper forest management," the forester said, "is that you can harvest again and again, often increasing the value of successive harvests. Done right, you can schedule another harvest in ten to fifteen years, about the same time you need to thin the pines again. Next time you would harvest fewer trees, but they will be of greater value."

"If we decide to cut, how would we proceed to set up a harvest?" asked Tom.

The forester handed Henry a pamphlet listing certified consulting foresters who provided service in area. "Look this over," she suggested. "You might also want to talk with some of your neighbors. There might be some nearby who also are interested in a timber sale, and you could work together and maybe get a better price for your timber. You might also want to talk with some who have had experience with consulting foresters in the area, and see who they liked and didn't like. There also is a local woodland owners group. Many members have very similar forests as yours, and several have harvested timber on their land. Also, here are some publications from University Extension which describe the aesthetics and wildlife considerations for harvesting or not harvesting."

"Couldn't we just go directly to a logger?" Henry asked.

"Yes, of course. But you'd be depending on the logger to deal with you honestly regarding what trees are cut and how much they are worth. To get the best deal, you should bid out your timber sale. A consulting forester can do that for you, and they can make sure you get a fair price and that the work is done properly. More importantly, the consulting forester will mark your timber and make sure the trees you want to save are not damaged."

"A couple more things," the forester added. "If you hire a consulting forester to guide you through the timber sale, and I recommend that you do, then ask about having them prepare a forest management plan to qualify you for the property tax deferment program. It would be quite a savings on your property taxes since about a third of your acreage is in forested land."

"How does a property tax deferment program work?" asked Henry.

"It is a program available in most states to encourage forest management. If you enroll your forested acreage, you can pay a small fraction of the normal property tax on that acreage each year. In the future, when you harvest timber, you would pay a severance tax that still would total less than what you otherwise would pay on your acreage. To qualify, you have to have an approved management plan which a certified consulting forester can prepare for you. Based on what we discussed today, I see no reason you wouldn't be eligible whether you decided on a regeneration cut or the tsi cut."

"But wouldn't we pay a severance tax right off the bat with the planned timber sale?" Tom asked.

"No. You could delay entering your forested acreage until after you've completed this harvest," the forester replied. Some states even allow you to make your initial harvest without the severance tax.

"Now, the second thing. I think you should have a management plan even if you don't sign up for property tax deferment or plan a harvest."

---

### FORESTED-PROPERTY TAX RELIEF

Depending on the age and species of your trees, it may take decades to realize any income from your woods, even if income is one of your goals. To encourage good forestry, and discourage exploitation of forests for short-term gains, many states have a program to reduce property taxes on forested land, or to defer taxes until timber is harvested. It is worth checking with your natural resource agency to see if you might benefit. (See Appendix 4)

---

"Why's that?" Henry asked, a bit defensively.

"I've given you some rough ideas about thinning your pines, and either a regeneration harvest or tsi harvest in your hardwoods. A management plan will flesh that out in more detail, and give you a "road map" for future management decisions. Among other things, it will suggest when you need to start thinking about another harvest, and might even project how much timber you could cut at that point. It also can include suggestions for improving aesthetics, wildlife habitat, species composition, or other potential benefits that can enhance your woods. You decide what you want and your priorities, and a professional forester can help you optimize the outcomes. If you do a harvest, the income will usually be treated as capital gains. You can subtract the cost of the consulting forester to reduce your income tax liability, so it is ideal to get the management plan done in conjunction with a timber sale."

"I have another question," Henry said. "Other than recommendations from neighbors, how else might I pick a consulting forester that will work well with us."

"You've bought a few cars in your time, I'll wager," the forester replied. "Have you ever walked away from a salesman because you didn't get the right vibes ?"

"Ha!" hooted, Tom, "You sure haven't looked for a car with my dad. I've been embarrassed more than once when he turned his back and walked away from a salesman."

"Well," said the forester, "getting the right consulting forester is a bit like buying a car. You have an idea of what you want, but there are so many details and some options with which you aren't familiar. Consulting foresters want to sell you their services. Although we have pretty good confidence in those listed in that pamphlet, they vary a lot. Don't be afraid to ask lots of questions, and don't be afraid to tell one to 'take a hike.' After all, you are going to pay for their services, and if you don't feel good about one, keep looking. There are lots of good consulting foresters and you can find the right one."

"By the way," she continued. "If you use a computer and have internet connection, you should check out the ForestryUSA website at www.forestryusa.com There you can find connections to just about every forestry-related topic, organization, industry, and state internet site there is, including emerging issues, consultants, and so forth."

"I did go on that site," Tom said, clearly pleased with himself. "It was very helpful."

"Thanks for your time," Henry replied. "I feel that I got some of my tax money back this morning."

"You're welcome," the forester said. "Don't hesitate to call if you have other questions . Good luck."

# Chapter 3
# Uncertainty and Anxiety

Henry was anxious about a timber sale, and was sure it would not resolve the inheritance issue. After all, he suggested to Rebecca that evening, "A portion of the value of the timber belongs as much to the girls as it does to Tom, so we can't just turn the money over to him, can we?"

"No, it doesn't seem right," Rebecca agreed, "and we don't want that ridge clear-cut."

"Even a clear-cut won't begin to bring in enough money to even things up anyway," Henry agreed. "I don't know what this place is now worth, but it's probably approaching a million dollars."

Henry and Rebecca discussed their concerns with Tom and Jean around the breakfast table. "There's got to be some way to keep the farm intact," Henry said, "and maybe getting some cash value from the forest will help, but I don't see that it solves our problem."

Several weeks later Jean sat down at the dinner table excited to share what she had learned while exploring ways to deal with the inheritance problem. Although a paralegal, she had never previously investigated options for transferring private property. She had used the internet to investigate options for transferring private property. "Have you ever heard of a limited liability company, often called a LLC?" she asked.

"Can't say that I have," Henry replied thoughtfully. "Me either," Rebecca added. They had come to appreciate their daughter-in-law's careful investigation of issues.

"Well, I think it's worth looking into," Jean said. "As I understand it, you could create an LLC with an Operating Agreement that all members of the family would sign. The LLC can be legally established for whatever period of time you wish, even 100 years or more, with legal ways to adjust as necessary. You can even include how the Company would be transferred from one set of members to a different set of members as the family changes. The charter would also include details on how liabilities and profits would be handled. This might be a way that Tom, Mary, and Beth would all continue to share the farm, along with their children and spouses, as you see fit. You and Tom can continue to be managers as you are now."

"Sounds like you might be onto something," Henry agreed. "Tom, maybe you and me should read up on it and be prepared to discuss it with Mary and Beth when we get together at Easter. Rebecca and me are going to that forest landowners meeting at the town hall on Thursday evening. I'll see if anyone there is familiar with an LLC."

At the meeting, Henry met several neighbors he knew, as well as some he had not met. The program was on invasive species that were starting to appear in local forests, and Henry learned how to recognize some of them. He was anxious to walk the woods again to see if he could spot any. He had a chance to talk with Homer Miller, who had a large woodlot about two miles from his. Homer said he'd be interested in walking his woods with the county forester to see if a timber sale might be in order and, if so, he'd talk with Henry about a joint timber sale. No one, however, knew anything about an LLC, so the next morning, Henry asked Jean to see if she could print off information from the internet or the public library.

That evening, Jean was ready with notes to discuss what she learned. "A limited liability company, or LLC," she explained, "was the simplest and most flexible of various ways to keep property within family ownership from one generation to another. An LLC can be dedicated to any purpose, from business to conservation, or various combinations."

"Well, that sounds good," Henry said.

"There are no limitations on the number of members an LLC can have," Jean continued. "Membership can be limited or members can be added when the other members, called founders, decide to include them, or even be fractional. Membership works just like ownership of shares in a corporation. To set up an LLC, the members prepare articles of organization which includes information such as the name, which must be followed by LLC to indicate the nature of the corporation, physical

---

### Land Division and Inheritance Options

Landowners have faced the issue of transferring land to heirs (usually one or more children) since property rights were developed. Transferring woods presents special problems because some members of the family are likely to develop a stronger bond to the trees than other family members, because the woods only occasionally generates income, and because accessible woodland is extremely valuable if sold for residential lots and even woodland with poor access has high sale value for hunting. In recent times many families have dealt with the issue proactively—with thoughtfulness and openness. You should consider all the options including novel ones such as a non-traditional life estate or a "Property Retention Trust." (See Appendix 5.)

---

location of the offices, name and location of the agent of process, and the fiscal year for bookkeeping purposes."

"So," Henry interjected, "Rebecca and me, Tom and you, Beth and her husband, and Mary and her husband could all be founders, each with a vote? And that could be changed by vote of the founders at any time?"

"That's my understanding," Jean replied. "You'd also need to state whether our LLC would be a member-managed or manager-managed LLC. I assume you could put Tom as manager if you wanted, or you could be manager, and that could change when members agreed to change it. I think you also state the 'term' of the LLC, such as 50 or 100 years. You also would indicate in the operating agreement how changes could be made in the agreement in the future."

"Once you've addressed these things, typically in a page or two, members sign and date it, including mailing addresses and phone numbers, then submit it to the Secretary of State with required filling fees. I think it takes a few weeks to get approval," Jean added.

"Once approved," the members would draft an operating agreement that explains the purpose, relationship of members to the LLC, and matters of governance."

"I'd guess it is in the operating agreement where members would specify how we'd go about making any changes, such as members, or manager, or whatever, and maybe how profits and debts would be handled," Henry suggested.

"That makes sense," Jean said. "Once the operating agreement is accepted, the founders would initiate transfer of title of the property to the LLC either directly, or as a trust of the LLC."

"I'd think we would want an attorney to look over the papers before we did that," Rebecca suggested.

"I'd think so," Jean replied. "Also, there is the question of vesting your heirs in the LLC. Because the farm is in your names, you'd need to transfer ownership to your heirs by making them members of the LLC and co-owners of the farm. This could be done gradually over several years to maintain tax-exemption. Once that is done, then your heirs become full-fledged members of the LLC with voting privileges accordingly. The farm is actually owned by the LLC at that point with risks and profits to be distributed however the members agree."

"That sounds like what we've been looking for," Henry said with some enthusiasm. "We should discuss it with an attorney before we get too far with it, however."

"What about the timber harvest then," Rebecca asked.

"I'm thinking we need to thin the pines regardless," Henry said. "So I'm going to start looking for a consulting forester to help us with that sale. If we find one we like, we can discuss the hardwoods with him and see if he agrees with that DNR forester. If we can harvest trees and help the forest all at the same time, and maybe get a management plan and a tax break, it seems like a good option."

"I'll sleep a little better tonight," Rebecca said. "But I think we also should explore an option that I heard about from Ed and Ellie Wheeler at the meeting the other night. None of their kids or grandchildren are interested in keeping their farm, yet Ed and Ellie want to protect it, especially the woods, forever, no matter who owns the property."

"How can they do that?" Tom asked.

"They used something called a conservation easement," Rebecca said. "Apparently, a conservation easement can be used to prohibit any future action on the property that they didn't want…like clear-cutting, or even the cutting of certain trees. I guess Ed and Ellie are doing some timber harvest themselves, but they want to prevent the old hemlocks, white pines and oaks from ever being cut," Rebecca continued.

"Ellie said the main purpose of the easement would be to prevent future subdivision of their property. In their case, they stipulated that one new lot could be surveyed out, but otherwise, no division."

"Well, wouldn't it be great to know that this old farm would remain long after we're all gone?" Henry said with enthusiasm. "

"There is a drawback," Rebecca added. "With restrictions of the

---

### CONSERVATION EASEMENTS

Family intentions may fade and government zoning that protected land from certain unwanted uses can change. A conservation easement is a way to protect your land-use values in perpetuity. The easement becomes part of the deed and remains with the property forever. The conditions of the easement are guarded by a Land Trust, an organization, often local, that will work with you to set up the easement. (See Appendix 6.)

---

easement, the market value of the property becomes less."

"That's a drawback only if you wanted to sell it," Tom suggested. "Seems to me, with lower value, you should get a property tax break."

"Ed said they did get a tax break," Rebecca agreed. "Not only are their property taxes less, they also could claim the reduced value of the property against their income taxes. He thought that wasn't always the case, however."

"How do you go about setting up a conservation easement?" Henry wanted to know.

"They got help from something called a land trust," Rebecca said. "I gathered a local land trust is an organization that oversees the conservation easement. Ed and Ellie created a small endowment in the land trust to cover the expense of the oversight."

"Although it sounds like a terrific idea, I'm surprised that Ed and Ellie figured it out. I thought that LLC was complicated enough," Henry sighed.

"I'm going to call the girls right now and see how they feel about what we should do with the farm and woods," Rebecca said as she got up. "It'll be bed time soon."

The next day as he sat down for lunch with his dad and mom Tom asked, "What did the girls have to say last night?"

"I'm so upset," Rebecca said. "Did you know Mary and Ben were having problems?"

"Yes," Tom replied. "Jean has talked with Mary a few times. Apparently, they may be getting a divorce, but we didn't think it was our place to tell you."

"That throws a wrinkle into things," Henry said. "It wouldn't do to have Ben a member of the LLC if he and Mary were divorced. He's never been very interested in what goes on around here anyway."

"Maybe the LLC should just include us and the kids," Rebecca suggested.

"What did they think about selling some of the timber," Tom persisted.

"Mary was pretty upset when I called, and I never got around to discussing that with her. Beth said her family was fine with the present arrangement, but if there was a timber sale, or if the farm title were transferred, she expected to be treated equally. She said they had no interest in farming, but were aware of the growing cash value of the farm. They want to retire early and build a retirement home in the country. Apparently they have talked about building on the ridge where they could look over the creek and Dad's hemlocks. Beth said they don't want any money, just a deed to half the woods. She thought Mary could get the other half and the rest of the farm would go to Tom and Jean."

"So she knew about Mary and Ben?" Henry asked.

"Yes, she knew."

"Did you talk with Beth about the LLC idea?" Henry asked.

"Yes. She wondered what kind of liability they would have, if the farm went into debt. I didn't know enough about that to answer her question. I got the impression that she and Randy don't want to be roped into any responsibility with the farm."

Henry didn't say anything for awhile. The worry lines on his forehead seemed more prominent. What seemed so promising at first, now looked as if it would lead to arguments and distrust. "I guess we have to get more information and lay out all the options," he said. "I think we can go ahead with hiring a consulting forester, and getting more information about the limited liability corporation. I'd also like to get more information about that conservation easement idea."

"Maybe we can gather that information and have it ready to discuss when we all get together at Easter," Tom added.

# Chapter 4
# What's Really Important

Easter was late, and Rebecca's daffodils were in full bloom when Beth, Randy and their boys arrived on Good Friday evening. Saturday was filled with preparations for Easter, much laughter, and chores. The boys liked to run around grandpa's woods when they visited. Henry was pleased that they asked about some of the spring ephemerals that were in bloom.

Henry explained, "Those flowers have only a few weeks, at most, from the time the ground thaws until the leaves of the trees cast a heavy shade over them. In that short period, they put up their leaves, capture enough sunlight to flower, set seed, and store energy to carry them through to next spring. The leaves are coming out on most trees now, so the spring woodland flowers are about done for the year."

The old farm house had five bedrooms. Early beds were a common target on Saturday evening. They were finishing breakfast when Mary arrived by herself on Sunday morning. After church, the good times continued over a ham dinner, but Mary's cheerfulness was tempered by her embarrassment about the divorce. No one mentioned Ben.

"It's such a nice day, let's all take a walk to the woods," Henry suggested over cake and ice cream. "The boys can wander off if they are inclined, and we adults can talk about the farm."

As they walked, Henry stopped often to explain what he and Tom had learned from the forester. Tom added some things he had learned from the internet. Jean reviewed what she had found out about a Limited Liability Corporation and Rebecca explained her understanding of the conservation easement option. They crossed the pasture to the pine plantation. Tom, Mary, and Beth laughed about hiding in the pines when they were kids, when the trees were not much taller than they were. They all agreed that thinning made good sense.

"I remember when we planted those trees, 45 years ago this spring," Henry said. "Wasn't it around Easter, Becky?"

"No, it wasn't," Rebecca replied. "We planted them the last week of March. I was four months pregnant with Tom, and you worried about me carrying buckets of trees as you put them in."

"We just wanted some pines to protect the creek," Henry said wistfully. "Never thought about cutting any."

The pines were too thick to easily walk through, so they skirted the east edge north to the creek, then followed the creek into the woods. Soon they reached the first of the big hemlocks. "There aren't many old hemlocks left around here," Henry said emphatically. "Nobody's gonna cut these if I have my say!"

No one would have said anything, even if they disagreed. They all understood and respected Henry's affection for the big hemlocks. Turning away from the creek, they headed up the slope where a few weeks earlier Henry had heard the gobbler. Trilliums were in full bloom near the creek, and higher on the slope, they found trailing arbutus. "Have you ever smelled these flowers?" Henry asked as he got down on his knees and put his nose close to one of the flowers.

They all remembered being asked that same question every spring as Henry pointed out the flowers of trailing arbutus. They all had smelled them, at Henry's urging, but did so again. Even Rebecca, with some help from Beth, got down on hands and knees, to examine the delicate pink and white flowers. Their subtle fragrance was somehow soothing, definitely a softer side of nature.

Henry was uneasy about explaining his thoughts concerning a timber harvest, and avoided it until they reached the ridge. "Tom and me have been talking about selling some timber," he began. "We talked with one of the DNR foresters who thought we should do some thinning in this woods, and the income might help us even out the inheritance more evenly among you kids."

Beth seemed anxious to share her position. "Randy and I are financially secure," she said. "We have 529s for the boys' college and we each have a decent pension. We want to sell our Highland Park house in the next few years, and thought about building a retirement home here, where we'd be close to you folks. We like the woods just the way they are, especially the large trees," Beth added, with a challenge in her voice.

Sensing the tension, Tom jumped in. "Well, we sure don't disagree about these big trees," he said. "How long you reckon they've been here, Dad?"

"I especially like those big trees with ashy bark and the big limbs," Mary said, pointing to one of the white oaks. "Are they the same age as the great big pines?"

"I don't know," Henry said, looking toward the top of one of the large white pines. "But I do know the pileated woodpeckers often drill nesting cavities in these old pines, and I expect they've been doing that for well over 100 years. I think the oaks live longer, on average, than white pine, and white pine can live more than 300 years. We had one blow down when you kids were little. I counted over 290 rings when I squared off the butt log so we could sell it. Whether we do a timber harvest here or not, we'll not cut the big pines or oaks."

Rebecca suggested they walk back to the house so they could continue the conversation around the kitchen table. It was there over the years that the family's conflicts usually got resolved, and the kitchen was a comfortable place for all of them.

Back at the house, Rebecca set out pitchers of ice water and lemonade. Henry, anxious to get some closure, launched right in. "I'd like to have each of you share your thoughts and hopes for the future of this place," he said. "I know we all love the farm, and we love one another. We've got to find a solution for the future we can accept, if not like. Tom, as the oldest, you go first."

"I've lived here my entire life, and this is the only home Jean and I have known since we were married," Tom said. "We'd hate more than I can put into words selling pieces of the farm. We've always thought this might continue to be home to Mike or Michelle after we're gone. At the same time, we want to be fair to everyone. We know how much Mom and Dad have agonized over how to do that."

"Beth," Henry asked, "What are your thoughts?"

"I pretty much explained them out in the woods," Beth responded. "Randy and I have planned for years to retire back in this community where we grew up…to simplify our lives in a rural environment away from the hectic pace and pollution of the big city. We want our grand-children to play in the same woods that Tom, Mary and I did. And who knows, maybe one of our boys might be interested in being a part-time farmer if neither Mike or Michelle want to stay on the farm." She hesi-tated, then added, "I guess we don't need to own half the woods if we are sure that the big white oaks and pines are not cut, and no other lots are created."

"Mary, we know your situation has changed recently. How does that fit into your new plans?" Henry prompted.

"Frankly, Dad, I need cash." Mary was always direct. "I've never wanted to move away from this community, but the bookstore barely supported us and we have only a little equity in our home. I guess it was lack of money, as much as anything, that got to Ben. You know he was never as set on staying here as I was. We've decided to divide everything even-up, and that means I'll have some debt to cover. I've got an opportunity to expand the bookstore, and I think if I developed a market niche focusing on local interests, history and hobbies…the sort of things that people around here are interested in, I can make a go of it. I love the farm, especially the woods, and I don't want to see it divided. I especially like the conservation easement idea that Mom talked about." I'd rather be poor than see the woods clear-cut or the farm subdivided. If you had some trees cut, like you said, that would help me with a new start, I'd be thankful."

"What about you, Becky?" Henry asked, turning to Rebecca.

"Before I die, I'd like to see some of the country and locate some cousins back in Croatia," she said. "But I don't want to do anything that might endanger the farm. If I never stepped foot from this place again, I'd still be happy."

Finally, Henry spoke for himself. "I love this place almost as much as I love each of you," he said. "I would sacrifice any of my hopes for the rest of my life if it would allow the farm to be saved. Your mother and me have had 47 years of happiness, most of it right here. We've been blessed, and we know it. Still, if I could, I'd like to take Becky to see some other places…to go to Croatia. I'd also like to look up some family in Sweden. We've got a bit of money saved and hoped that we might go to Europe for our 50th wedding anniversary."

The mood had shifted from adversarial to fraternal. Wiping a few tears from her eyes, Rebecca got up to get some cheese and crackers to hide her emotions. No one spoke for a moment. Everyone's position was clearly stated and reasonable. Tom needed land to farm without heavy payments to his parents or sisters. Beth had a lot of emotional capital invested in retiring on the same land where she grew up. Mary needed cash, soon. Henry and Rebecca would like a little money for a late-life adventure.

Finally, Henry spoke. "Can we agree to go ahead with thinning the pines?"

No one objected.

"Seems like none of us want to see the land divided," he continued, drawing attention to the points of agreement. Everybody nodded their heads.

"And it seemed to me we all agreed to protect the woods along the creek with the big hemlocks." Again, everyone nodded. "What about cutting about a third of the trees along the ridge?" Henry asked.

"Only if those big pines and oaks are saved," Mary chimed in. Again, everyone nodded.

Henry turned to Beth. "If you get half the woods for your retirement home, Mary will have to clear-cut the other half to get her cash, or even sell her half."

A pained look crossed Beth's face. Tom added, "If the woods were sold, Jean and I would be much less interested in continu-ing with the farm. I can't imagine having a road running through the farm to the woods, especially with strangers coming and going.  I'm sure I can find work, and with Jean's job, we'd either buy a place or build."

Rebecca was uneasy with the heightened tension. "Would a con-servation easement resolve anything?" she asked. "It makes me sick to think about houses back on the ridge."

Beth and Randy had been whispering. Randy spoke up. "Although it was a dream of ours, Beth and I don't have to build on the ridge. We'd like a spot where we could view the woods, perhaps, maybe out of sight of the farmhouse. More important than building there, we want to preserve the beauty of the woods like the rest of you. If we can agree on protecting the woods now, then it will be important to us to have some legal agreement that some future problem doesn't arise. We think a conservation easement would do it, and maybe the Limited Liabil-ity Corporation would be helpful to transfer farm ownership. A careful timber harvest makes sense to us to provide cash for Mary and for the folks. All we need is a deeded lot somewhere for our house."

Henry glanced toward Rebecca. The exchange between them might have been missed by the others, but each took note of the relief in the other's face. They were on the threshold of a solution to a problem that had worried them for months.

"So we can go ahead with thinning pines and setting up a limited timber sale," Tom summarized. "We should also look further into a conservation easement, and we might as well agree on where Beth and Randy's lot is going to be so we can include that information in the easement papers."

Jean finally spoke. "The cash from the timber sale for Mary and a small lot for Beth and Randy's house is not an equitable share of the value of the farm," she pointed out. "It is important to Tom and me that everyone feel they have been treated fairly so that there won't be hard feelings later. The only way I can see to do that while keeping the farm intact is through a LLC."

"Yes," Rebecca agreed. "I think we should discuss the LLC with a lawyer while we're exploring the conservation easement."

Mary looked like a burden had been lifted from her as well. Her siblings and parents had been non-judgmental about her failed marriage and it looked like she could count on some cash in the near future. She also was pleased that not only Tom, but also Beth would be physically close to her parents as they aged. On top of all that, the woods and the big trees that were more important to her than she'd ever realized would be protected, hopefully forever.

# Chapter 5
# Finding the Right Forester

Sunday evening, after everyone had left, Henry sat down with the DNR pamphlet and began making a short list of consulting foresters. He hoped to find someone local, or at least near enough to minimize travel costs. His top priority, however, was to find a consultant who could appreciate his family's interests in protecting aesthetic and conservation values of their forest. There wasn't enough information given to make that judgment, so he figured he'd need to interview several and sort that out over the phone.

After chores on Monday, Henry began phoning those on his list. His first call was to Hugh Tower who listed a local number. The phone rang only twice before Tower answered.

"Mr. Tower, this is Henry Chapel," Henry began. "My son, Tom, and me operate a farm here in the county. We have a small pine plantation that needs to be thinned, and about 35 acres of hardwoods that the country forester recommended for a timber stand improvement harvest. I'm looking for a consulting forester who can help us prepare a management plan and oversee the timber sale." Henry went on to give the location of the farm and briefly describe the forest.

"I'd be glad to work with you," Tower replied. "Would you like to make an appointment for us to take a look at your woods?"

"I've got a couple questions first," Henry said. "Have you done a management plan or conducted a timber sale for anyone near here?"

"I wrote a management plan and set up a timber sale for Johnson Creek Farms a few years ago," Tower replied. "They are about ten miles

north of your place. If you'd like, I can send you a list of client references. You can contact any of them."

"Have you worked with mature hardwoods where most of the big
trees were left?" Henry wanted to know.

"No...." Tower was hesitant. "I don't recommend allowing hardwoods to get very old. Once their growth has slowed down, they are
more prone to disease, decay, and begin to lose value. The most productive hardwoods are young to intermediate-aged trees."

"So in managing mature oaks, you'd generally recommend clear-
cutting or at least some form of regeneration harvest?" Henry prompted.

"Generally, yes," Tower replied.

"Well, thanks for your time," Henry said, and promptly hung up.

His second call was to Jim Powers, Forestry Consultants, in the
county seat. A woman answered. "I'd like to speak with Mr. Powers,"
Henry said.

"May I tell him who's calling and the reason for your call?" the woman asked politely.

"Yes. I'm looking for a forester to help my son and me develop a forest management plan and set up a timber sale," Henry said.

A minute later, "Jim Powers speaking. How can I help you, Mr. Chapel?"

"Please call me Henry." Henry went on to explain his situation and
asked Powers about his recommendations for mature hardwoods. The
conversation didn't go well.

"Henry, I'd never recommend a selection cut in mixed hardwoods
where you'd hope to regenerate oaks. You can select some of the big
trees around the edges, or even some groups of trees to leave, but you
should plan to get your money out of the mature timber before it starts
to deteriorate. You'll be much more successful regenerating the oaks."

"One more thing," Powers went on. "We work on a commission,
not the clock. We'll negotiate a percentage of the timber sale depending
on the estimated value of the stumpage and how long it will take us to
prepare the sale and the management plan. You won't have to lay out a
dime."

That clinched it for Henry. "Thank you for your time," he said, and
hung up. Wasn't it clear to others that there would be a conflict of interest if a forester set up a timber sale based on a percentage of the
stumpage sold, Henry wondered. The fact that Powers seemed set on a
heavy harvest rather than a careful timber stand improvement harvest
seemed to prove the point.

---

## Hiring a Consulting Forester

Few people would undertake legal action without consulting an attorney, or building a house without consulting an architect or professional builder. A forest management plan is comparably complex with both biological and legal ramifications. A good management plan well executed can enhance property values and increase the income and other benefits you derive from your forest. Consulting foresters have the education and training to work with you to achieve your goals for your forest, but as with any professional, some may be better suited for your work than others. (See Appendix 7.)

---

The third call was equally discouraging. "I'm beginning to think it might be best to just let the woods alone," he muttered to himself as he dialed Clarence Paine, the fourth name on the list.

" Paine speaking," came the prompt response. "How can I help you?"

Again Henry introduced himself, and asked about references and hardwood management. "Call me Chuck," Paine inserted. "May I call you Henry?"

"Nearly everyone does," Henry replied.

"Henry, you are the person to decide what you want from your forest," Chuck began. "I can help you see the possibilities and reach you goals, assuming they are reasonable. If you want to leave most of your big trees, that will obviously reduce the monetary income from your forest, but you apparently have other priorities, and that's just fine with me."

After ten minutes of lively give and take, Henry and Chuck agreed on a day and time to walk the forest.

A week later, Chuck drove in five minutes before the time he and Henry had agreed to meet. Henry sized him up as he walked toward his truck. The truck was relatively new, and clean, although it had recently been driven on a muddy road. Chuck was talking on his cell phone, and leafing through his appointment book. On the back of the passenger seat hung an orange vest with two mechanical pencils protruding, and several bulges suggesting other equipment or gear that Henry couldn't identify. Chuck appeared to be in his late 20s, with short-cropped hair, and a neatly pressed shirt. As Henry approached, he put his cell phone in the holster on his belt, picked up a hard hat from the passenger-side seat, and stepped out of his truck with his orange vest.

"Henry?" Chuck asked, as he stuck out his hand.

"Yep, that's me," Henry responded as they shook hands. "I appreciate a person who is on time."

"Well, I make an effort to be punctual," Chuck replied with a wry smile, "but I can't claim to always succeed. I'm glad to meet you, Henry. Where would you like to start?"

"If you don't mind," Henry responded, "I'd like to talk a bit before we go to the woods. I've got some reluctance to do any cutting in my woods."

"Of course," the forester replied. "I'd much prefer to work with an owner who values his woods than someone who didn't. In my opinion, good forestry begins with a love of the land and respect for the plants and animals in our woods."

Tom walked up as Chuck was speaking. "Chuck, this is my son, Tom. He and I pretty much run the farm with some help from my grandson, Mike. Tom, this is Chuck Paine, a consulting forester. We're just getting acquainted."

"Pleased to meet you," Chuck said as he stuck out his hand.

"I like what you said," Henry continued. "My wife, Becky, and I have worked this farm for nearly 50 years, and it's like an extension of our family. I expect I've laid eyes on nearly every tree back on that ridge. The thought of some yahoo in a big machine ripping the heart out of that woods with no regard except how much money he could make is a nightmare. Is it possible to get a logger who will be sensitive to our management priorities?"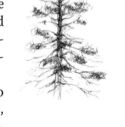

"Yes," Chuck said thoughtfully, "but you need to understand that cutting timber is a messy business, even when done well. If done right, however, the forest can soon repair any damage from logging and it can be healthier, more productive, and even more aesthetically pleasing".

"Years ago, this part of the country was all forested," he continued. "Settlers came in and cut down trees, ripped out or burned stumps, and began planting corn and other crops. That was an even messier business. Fortunately, they left some of the forests, like yours. These remaining forests have become increasingly valuable. They protect water quality, provide wildlife habitat, timber products, and aesthetics, among other things. Back then, the focus was on getting the resource from the woods. We now know a lot more about how to optimize the many benefits we receive from a forest without exploiting it. Unfortunately, there are still some who would rather maximize their short-term profits than manage sustainably. They give forestry a bad reputation."

Neither Henry nor Tom said anything for a minute. Finally, Henry said, "I'm glad I called you, Chuck. I think you can help us. Let's go take a look at the woods."

"Do you have a map of the farm?" Chuck asked. "Perhaps a map showing the soil types, or an NRCS map? You probably get some federal subsidy on some of your crops."

"Yes, we've got the NRCS map that labels our fields and shows the acreage," Henry replied. "Do you need a copy?"

"Not now," Chuck responded. "I can download the soils map for your farm from the internet, but I need a plat or some map that shows the property boundaries along the woods. If we proceed with a timber sale, I'll also need to check your deed for a legal description of your property. We'll want to make sure a logger doesn't trespass, so I'd want to mark any property lines adjacent to any planned logging activity."

"What is the first step?" Tom asked.

"First, I'll prepare a draft management plan for your forested acres," Chuck answered, "assuming you want me to be your consulting forester," he added with his characteristic boyish smile.

A hint of smile appeared at the corners of Henry's eyes. "I assume we'd sign a contract to that effect before proceeding," he said. "But how do you go about doing a management plan?"

"I have a good sense of your priorities for your woods already," Chuck said. "But as we walk, I'd like to have you continue to talk about what you'd like your woods to be, even pointing out individual trees you'd like left...just to give me a clearer picture. Maybe there are some special areas you want protected from logging, or some species you'd like to favor."

"Hemlocks along the creek, for starters!" Tom injected. "Dad don't want them cut."

"We'll take a look," the forester replied. "Generally, we'd want to leave a buffer of undisturbed forest along the creek anyway. But let's get back to the management plan. You asked how I'd proceed."

"I'll use a geographic information system, or GIS for short, to overlay soil types on an air photo of your wooded acres. I can also put in topography, streams, roads, or even special areas you want protected. Today, I'll be deciding if the soil types, slopes, and timber warrant dividing the woods into different management areas. We want to customize management to the potential of the forest so that you can optimize the outcome, whether it is aesthetics, wildlife, timber, diversity, or whatever you want."

"For each management area, perhaps just the pine plantation and the hardwoods if there isn't a need to divide the hardwood area, I'll include a description and some tables of data on what is there now. I'll include recommendations for what management treatments are needed and approximately when, including any harvest. If a harvest is recommended, I'll indicate in a general way, how it should be done. The specifics will go into a timber sale contract. The management plan will clearly indicate your priorities for the forests, and any special concerns or restrictions. Everything will be referenced to the map."

They had reached the pine plantation. Chuck stepped through the fence, and disappeared into the pines as Henry and Tom waited. "I really have a good impression of this young guy," Henry said. "He not only seems to know his business, but he understands and appreciates how we value the woods."

Tom and Henry continued talking as they walked slowly along the edge of the pines. Ten minutes passed before Chuck emerged a 100 yards in front of them.

"There's no question a thinning is needed," he said as they approached. "I agree that a row thinning is the best way to proceed with this first cut. Did you know there were some hardwoods crowding in on the west side?"

"No, I haven't been in that far in several years, I suppose," Henry replied.

"Most are box-elders," Chuck said, "but there are a few white ash and black cherries. I'd suggest we have the logger who does the thinning drop them. They will interfere with the pines, and won't amount to much anyway."

"Don't they contribute to diversity?" Tom wanted to know.

"Yes, but in plantation management, it is very hard to keep both hardwoods and conifers. Often, the conifers will outgrow and overtop the hardwoods. Sometimes the hardwoods get far enough ahead that they will persist. A logger that buys pulpwood or even conifer sawtimber generally doesn't want to mess with the odd hardwood that might be mixed in the sale. Some plantations are established with mixed rows of conifers and hardwoods, but again, they often are less successful because of different growth rates. In this case, you have all red pine, and the few hardwoods are simply intruders. Years from now, you may want to consider converting this plantation to hardwoods, especially if many begin to get established under the pines. But for now, I'd remove them although you could leave a few cherries along the edges."

"Any other questions?" Chuck asked.

"So the management plan for the plantation will suggest when the next harvest should be?" Tom asked.

"Yes, it will be pretty simple at this point," Chuck said. "There isn't a whole lot of variation in the growth rates in the plantation, and other than those hardwoods, I think we simply indicate a thinning in the next three years, then again in about 10 years. Management plans need to be reviewed and revised about every 10 to 15 years, and that's when we'd need to make some more decisions about the future of the plantation."

They entered the woods along the creek near where the big hemlocks grew. Glancing at the water, Chuck observed, "This creek looks to be pretty high quality. Must not be very much farming upstream, or at least, farmers are protecting the creek from runoff and livestock."

"There's a lot of wetlands not far, and I think the creek comes mostly from there," Henry said. "I only know of two farms up-stream, and they seem to be pretty careful."

"There's a big hemlock there," Chuck pointed out. "I can see why you'd not like to cut them. I'll bet that tree is at least 200 years old."

"There's some species along the creek that don't occur upslope," Henry said. "There's even a decent-sized butternut further down, and several bitternut hickories."

"I think you'd be wise to keep a pretty good strip of forest undisturbed along here," Chuck said. Tom and Henry nodded in agreement. "It is possible for a good logger to reach in here with a boom or a cable and lift or skid trees away from the creek with minimal disturbance, but unless you are trying to squeeze every dollar out of this woods that you can, it isn't really the best practice. Better to leave the forest to protect the creek and provide you the pleasure you get from it."

"How do you keep a logger from taking trees he isn't supposed to?" Henry wanted to know.

"Once we decide what you want, I'll come in and put paint on trees to be harvested. I'd also paint the boundaries of the sale with a different colored paint, typically blue, so the logger knows when he is near the edge. We'd put pretty severe penalties in the contract for taking trees that are not marked for cutting."

"If you're not here to watch, how do you know if they take unmarked trees," Tom asked.

"Good question," Chuck said. "A good logger doesn't want to risk his reputation by taking an unmarked tree. But to make sure, we mark the trees at about eye height where it is easy for the logger to see, usually on two sides, then we also put a paint mark near the ground. If I find a stump without a paint mark when I check on the logger, I know he took an unmarked tree. The penalty will stipulate either a handsome fixed dollar amount or sometimes we stipulate three times the estimated value of the tree based on the stump."

"Do you have to paint the boundary along the creek," Henry asked. "I don't fancy having to look at painted trees for years to come."

"I can flag the boundary with plastic tape," Chuck said. "Once the logging is completed, I'll pull down the flagging. It is common to give loggers two years to complete a sale, especially when they are restricted to frozen-ground harvesting, although this is small enough that I'd be surprised if they didn't get right on it after we complete a contract. If they waited a year or two, I might have to re-hang flagging before they started cutting, but that would be a minor task."

Chuck took out a prism and began making observations and taking notes. Henry and Tom observed that he proceeded in a systematic way through the woods, following a compass line, similar but more thorough than the county forester did. Periodically, Henry would point out a tree that he particularly liked. He also pointed out a bee tree, a tree with a small hole 20 feet up where honey bees were coming and going He said he'd not like to see the wild bees disturbed by the logging. Chuck made a note, and using a GPS instrument, noted the location.

Two hours later, they gathered at Chuck's truck. "It will take me a week or two to work up these data and draft your management plan," he said. "I'll mail it to you and we can find a time to get together for a couple of hours after you've looked it over. If you'd like your wives or other family members to set in on that meeting, that would be fine with me. We can meet in the evening, if you wish."

"Thanks so much for your time and understanding," Henry answered. "You've opened my eyes to a lot of possibilities already, and given me the assurances that I needed to go ahead with management on our forests."

"Great! I'll be in touch soon," the forester replied as he climbed in his truck.

# Chapter 6
# A Good Plan

A week passed during which Henry and Tom prepared the corn ground, then serviced the haybine and the bailer in preparation for haying. Tom also found a few hours to get a nice 22-pound gobbler that he shot along the south edge of the woods. Rebecca took a picture of Tom and his turkey, using the new digital camera that Jean had given him for Christmas.

"You got a large envelop in the mail from that consulting forester," Rebecca told Henry when he came in for lunch. Henry opened it before he sat down. At the top, was "D R A F T" in bold letters. What followed was pretty much what Chuck had told Henry and Tom to expect (See Appendix 9.) "Come eat before it gets cold!" Rebecca scolded, as Henry poured over the draft. "You can digest that report later."

"It's not a report," Henry said. "It's the draft of a management plan for our forest."

"Well, how does it look?" Rebecca wanted to know.

"Good. It's exactly what Chuck said it would be. You know, the surprising thing to me is how straightforward it is. There's nothing too complicated about it, yet it provides some clear indications of what and when we need to be doing some management activities in the woods. I'll go over it more carefully this evening, then we'll want to discuss it with Tom before setting up an appointment with Chuck." Henry dipped a spoon into his bowl of vegetable soup, and thoughtfully swallowed it, savoring the flavor, before adding, "I sure do like that young man. I'd about decided no forester could understand the way we value the woods, but Chuck did, and he seems to really know forestry."

"Well, I'm relieved," Rebecca said. "I know how you've worried about managing the woods. How's the soup?"

"Good, as usual," Henry said with a smile, tossed casually toward Rebecca. "I'll continue to worry about the woods until we find a good logger and get that taken care of. I trust Chuck to help with that, too."

That evening, Henry spent an hour pouring over the draft plan. He took out a pad of paper and pencil and began writing questions he and Tom wanted to go over with Chuck. After an hour he reviewed his list:

1. What does 2-0 mean in connection to the pines we planted?

2. Why do you mention that the pines have 20% live crown? They seem healthy.

3. Why do you mention wind, snow-loading, etc. in connection with removing every third row of pines?

4. You indicate utilization of pines down to 3 inches or 4 inches. What does that mean?

5. How do you decide what a "crop tree" is?

6. What does "thin from below" mean?

7. What is tsi, and how would you determine which mature trees to harvest?

8. I'm still not clear what basal area is, and why it is so important?

9. Why would you reduce basal area so much (nearly 40%)?

10. What does stumpage mean?

11. What is a northern pin oak, and why is it lumped with black oak rather than red oak?

12. How is cable skidding done?

13. Why have you limited so severely when the logging can occur?

14. How would I recognize an invasive species? What ones should I especially keep a look out for?

The following day, Henry shared the report with Tom, and the two of them reviewed Henry's list of questions. Tom recalled that "tsi" was an abbreviation for "timber stand improvement," but he couldn't remember what that involved. Harvesting seemed counter-intuitive to timber stand improvement, but he guessed that it meant the poorest trees would be removed, leaving the best trees to grow.

At noon, Henry called Chuck Paine and they agreed to meet the following Monday evening at 7:00 at the house. He told Chuck that he'd invited Homer Miller, his neighbor who also had some woods that he thought might profit from management.

Homer had indicated some weeks back that he'd be interested in a timber sale at the same time if it would increase the money they could get for their trees. Henry knew that Chuck would be opposed to setting up a harvest in Homer's woods without a management plan, and he hoped Homer would be as pleased as he was with Chuck's approach to forestry. Maybe, he thought, if Homer sat in when they reviewed the draft plan with Chuck, he'd see how easy it was.

Homer and his wife, Arlene, arrived Monday evening at 6:45, as Henry was still showering and changing clothes. Rebecca was talking with them at the kitchen table when Henry came down. Tom and Jean came in a few minutes later. At 7:03 Henry heard Chuck's truck pull in the driveway, and went to the porch to greet him.

"How are you, Henry?" Chuck said, offering his hand.

"Good! Come on in," Henry replied, holding the door open.

After introductions, Chuck took a seat at the table and pulled out a copy of Henry's draft management plan from his well-used briefcase. He also pulled out a larger copy of the map of the two forest tracts and spread it on the table. "I thought we might want to review some things so I brought a scaled-up copy of the map that is in the draft plan," he said.

Henry pulled out his list of questions, and noticed that a surprised look crossed Chuck's face. "Why the surprise?" he asked.

"I've had people ask me lots of questions at this stage," Chuck said with his boyish smile, "but no one ever had a written list as long as yours."

"Well, maybe I'm a slow learner," Henry said, with a twinkle in his eyes.

"On the contrary," Chuck came back, "I'm pleased that you are so interested. It actually makes my job easier."

"How do Henry's questions make your job easier?" Rebecca asked. "He can be a pain with all his questions," she added, with tenderness.

"Well, I see my job as helping you get all the benefits you'd want from your forest," Chuck replied. "The more I learn about your interests and values, the easier it is for me to guide your management in a way that increases those benefits."

Turning to Homer, Henry said, "Now you see why I like this guy. I've only talked to a handful of professional foresters, but some seemed to think of my woods as their meal-ticket. Chuck here seems more interested in helping us do a better job managing our woods."

"Maybe we'd better discuss my contract before you completely make up your mind," Chuck said with a grin. He pulled out another sheet of paper and handed it to Henry. "Let's review this before getting to the management plan."

At the top of the page were Chuck's name, address, phone number, and email address. The opening paragraph briefly explained that this was a contract for forest management services. There were a few conditions itemized:

1. Direct expenses, including travel at $0.45/mile, would be itemized in a monthly statement.

2. Time, excluding travel, would be billed at a rate of $55 per hour. Travel time would be billed at $27.50 per hour.

3. A monthly bill would be prepared following completion of work, and payment was expected within 30 days.

3. All recommendations would comply with best management practices, legal requirements, and sustainable forest management knowledge.

Services to be provided would include a forest management plan, with recommended management practices and time-lines suggested for the next ten years. Additional services, such as marking and administering a timber sale, would be offered at the same rate, and an estimate would be provided on request. At the bottom were places for both Chuck and Henry to sign and date.

"This seems reasonable," Henry said. "How much do we have already invested in the draft management plan?"

Chuck pulled out a pocket notebook and leafed through it, briefly. "My first visit was free," he said. "When I came back to get some additional inventory data on your woods, it took me 45 minutes driving time, 36 miles, and 2 hours field time. I took an hour to prepare the map and an hour to complete the draft plan. There were no direct expenses. That comes to $168.07. I'll charge you for only an hour this evening, if Rebecca can rustle up a cup of coffee," he added with a wink at Rebecca. "That will make the total $213.07."

"I spent nearly twice that to fill our diesel tank today," Henry said with a pained look. "It is a bargain given the peace of mind I will have about taking care of the woods. What do you figure it will cost to set up and administer that timber sale?"

"I can only give you a rough estimate off the top of my head," Chuck said. "Based on similar sales, with marking, advertising, reviewing bids, and overseeing the work, I'd estimate that we're looking at something a bit less than $1000. Based on your desire for a tsi harvest, which means leaving the most valuable trees, I'd guess your total sale will provide you with roughly $20,000. So my services would be on the order of five per cent. Of course, you understand, I don't operate on a percentage," he quickly added.

"Could I ask a question?" Homer chimed in.

"Of course," Chuck said, with his characteristic grin, "but you're on Henry's nickel."

"I've got a woodlot about the same size as Henry's, maybe a bit bigger. I don't have a creek to deal with. Would a forest management plan cost me about the same as Henry's? And would he and I both get a bit more if we offered our timber for sale to the same buyer?"

"Yes, to both questions," Chuck replied. "By doubling the amount of timber to be sold, with minimal cost for moving equipment, a buyer could offer a better price. My time would be slightly less since I'd mark both pieces on the same trip, and I would only need to put out one advertisement for the sale. I'd really need to walk your woods before giving you any more specific information, however. Also, I won't administer a timber sale for you until you have an acceptable management plan,"

Conversation continued while Rebecca got coffee and a plate of cookies. Homer and Chuck agreed to meet on Wednesday afternoon to walk his woods and discuss management options. Henry and Chuck signed two copies of the contract for consulting services, one of which Henry handed to Rebecca for their farm records, commenting that the cost could be written off as a farm business expense.

They then turned to Henry's questions from the draft management plan. Chuck explained that 2-0 seedlings were the most common for red pine plantings. That meant the seedlings were grown in the nursery for two years, and had not been transplanted. A 2-1 seedling would have been three years old, two years in the nursery bed and one year in a transplant bed. Because they are larger, 2-1 trees require more time to plant. Their larger roots prevented easy use of a spud or planting bar, although when planting machines were used, this was less of a problem. Survival might actually be poorer, Chuck explained, because the tree had more leaf exposure and it takes a bit of time for roots to develop good contact with the soil. Especially if a drought occurred early in the growing season after planting, survival of trees could be lower.

"Why would anyone pay extra for 2-1 trees?" Henry asked.

"If growing conditions are good, they get a faster start," Chuck said, "and can tolerate more competition from weeds. If you control weeds until trees get a good start, there would be little difference between 2-0 and 2-1 trees after ten years," he speculated.

The 20% live crown indicated that the trees were too crowded.

Ideally, for good growth, red pines should have a minimum of 25% live crown, and better, 35%. "What does the percent live crown mean?" Tom asked.

"It means the percentage of the total tree height on which living limbs are growing," Chuck explained. "Your trees are about 50 feet tall, and have only about 10 feet of their height with living limbs."

"How will thinning change that?" Tom wanted to know.

"With more light, the remaining pines will increase their growth rate, and more limbs will continue to live," Chuck answered. "As the trees get taller, with new growth, the percentage of live crown will increase. Red pine, however, will never produce live limbs lower on the stem where shading has resulting in premature death of foliage."

Chuck went on to explain that trees that have been crowded for as long as theirs were spindly and much more subject to breakage from wind or snow loading. Trees that are crowded tend to grow nearly as fast in height, but do not increase stem diameter as fast as less-crowded trees. With weaker stems then can be bent more easily by snow- or ice-loading. He didn't think taking every third row would result in much damage, although a heavy ice storm or wet snow the first year or two after thinning might cause some loss.

In estimating yield, he looked at the number of 100-inch "sticks," the standard length pulp mills required, that could be cut from a tree. The 50-foot trees tapered toward the top. Nearly all would provide three 100-inch sticks, and most four or five sticks. It varied depending on the diameter at the small end. Mills preferred the small end to be no less than four inches in diameter. Most, however, would not complain if some sticks with three-inch ends were included, especially red pine. In part, it had to do with the mill, and in part, with the logger and his relationship with the mill. If he sold a lot of pulp, and had a good reputation of providing sound wood, the mill might be a bit more tolerant.

"Now, for the fun question," Chuck went on, with his characteristic smile. "A crop tree? It is what you want it to be." The puzzled looks that crossed the faces around the table were expected.

"For example, if I am correct that your highest priority in management is to maintain health and vigor of your forest, a crop tree could be any tree that isn't diseased or which doesn't contribute to poor health of surrounding trees. If aesthetics are important, then a crop tree might be any that you find especially attractive. (See Appendix 8. ) Some trees are more valuable for wildlife, and might be left as "crop trees" primarily for that reason. The term, of course, reflects the financial bias of forestry, and originated in conjunction with timber management. With crop tree management, we'd mark a stand such as yours with all these in mind, leaving the trees that are most important to achieve your objectives, and providing highest priority trees with room to grow."

"That makes a lot of sense to me," Henry said. "It's like keeping the best cows and a number that we can provide sufficient feed to keep healthy."

"Exactly! The difference, of course, is that your interests in the woods are far more complex, generally, than your interest in your cows. That makes forest management more challenging, but more interesting. Also, you're not just managing one species, but several species of trees, and you are also interested in dozens of other species in your woods....spring flowers and birds for example."

Chuck went on to explain that "thin from below" referred to removing smaller trees that were crowding larger, crop trees. A mature tree was one whose growth had tapered off to the point that it would not respond very much to being given more room to grow. Those likely to die within the next ten years, or which were diseased, deformed, or were species that contributed less to the highest priorities for the woods were the ones that a tsi harvest would most likely remove, especially if they were crowding trees that served the highest priorities of the owners.

"How about basal area? What does that mean?" Tom wanted to know.

"I won't go into the mathematics or theory of it," Chuck said, "but in brief, basal area is the total cross-sectional area of all the trees in a unit area, usually an acre in United States, or a hectare in most of the rest of the world. Foresters use "breast height" as a convention for measuring diameters and cross-sectional areas of trees, primarily because it is a convenient height and it is generally above the butt-swell of trees, where diameter or cross-sectional area is inflated. If you were to cut off all the trees in an acre at 4.5 feet above the ground, and totaled the cross-sectional area of the stumps, that would be the basal area."

"Isn't that difficult to measure?" Tom asked, "especially since you aren't actually cutting the trees off."

"It would be time-consuming if you actually had to measure all the diameters, and calculate areas," Chuck agreed. "Foresters use an angle gauge, usually a prism, to take a sample of trees proportional to their diameter. Because large trees contribute proportionately more basal area, the angle gauge samples them more often. This is where the mathematics gets complicated, but with a prism , I was able to estimate the basal area of your woods with reasonable accuracy in less than an hour. Of course, I broke it down by species, simply by noting the species of each tree the prism indicated that I should tally."

"Why is cross-sectional area so important," Tom persisted.

"It's not, really," Chuck replied, "but it is strongly correlated with the total canopy cover or volume of trees in that reference area. We use basal area because it is quick and easy to estimate, and provides us with a good estimate of total tree volume per acre."

"So how do you know how much basal area should be left in the woods? Henry wanted to know.

"We use experience plus some rules to guide us," Chuck explained. "On these soils, which are well-drained and productive, trees will make pretty good growth with 90 to 100 square feet of basal area per acre. You've got nearly 140 square feet up there. I'm suggesting a target of 85, to allow some room for growth before you need to come back and thin again. When I mark the stand for harvest, I'll be guided by the objectives you want for your forest, and aim to thin until we get close to an average of 85 square feet per acre."

"There is a caveat," he continued. "Opening up the forest will encourage some understory growth…things like blackberries, raspberries, and sprouts off of some trees, especially red maple. The amount varies from forest to forest, and is somewhat unpredictable, depending on past history in that forest. The tops of harvested trees, plus the understory development will make it more difficult for you to move about the woods for awhile. Of course wildlife, such as deer and turkeys, will like it. In a few years, as the tree canopy closes again, and as the tops rot down, the forest understory will open up."

"Is there any way to minimize the understory growth?" Tom asked.

"Yes, one could remove fewer trees in the harvest, and maintain more canopy," Chuck replied. "Of course, if you do that, you would get a lower price for your stumpage, and it would be necessary to come back to harvest more frequently, to maintain good growing conditions for crop trees."

"Well, we like the wildlife," Henry said, "and I don't fancy having loggers in the woods so often. Guess I'd prefer to have raspberries and turkeys."

Chuck went on to explain that stumpage referred to the value of timber that could be harvested. Northern pin oak was a limby species of oak that occurred in the region, but which frequently hybridized with black oak and red oak, more desirable species for timber and aesthetics. Because limbs leave knots in the wood, and made it more difficult to prepare for the mill or split for firewood, many people preferred black oak or red oak which nearly always occurred on the same sites. Red oak is more preferred by most people for its aesthetics, and brings a higher price, Chuck said.

"Around here, black and red oak hybridize to the point that it is sometimes difficult to decide whether it's one or the other," Chuck concluded. "On average, the pin oak is more similar to black oak, however, and they are more comparable in value, so that's why they are combined."

Cable logging, he explained, involved skidding the logs uphill using a cable attached to a winch. Skidders have winches with cables that could easily reach most of the logs from near the ridge line, and that would prevent the skidder from having to run up and down the slope. With good snow cover, that was less a concern, but some rutting ordinarily still occurred. If skidding were to occur without frozen or snow-covered ground, it would be even more important to avoid gouging the slope with skid trails.

Chuck said that because oak wilt is a fungus disease, with spores spread by beetles attracted to injured trees during the growing season, it is important to do the felling and skidding during the winter, when the fungus would not be spread to healthy trees.

"Are you saying that there will be injury to remaining trees?" Henry asked with concern.

"Yes. There always is some, even if only a few limbs broken on residual trees during felling," Chuck replied. "We'll put a penalty clause in the logging contract that will cause the logger to be more careful, but some damage is inevitable, even with the best, most careful loggers.

Broken limbs especially. I'll be much more concerned with skinning the bark of remaining trees during skidding. That is more a result of careless operation."

"It's getting late," Chuck finished. "How about we discuss invasive species some other time? I'll bring you some pictures of the most common problems in this area, and if you'd like to take a ride some day, we'll go find examples nearby. Are you folks okay with the priorities I've listed in the draft plan?" (Appendix 9).

"We think they reflect our interests pretty well," Henry said. "I think they are more on a par, than strict priorities, especially 2, 3 and 4. Otherwise, we're fine with the plan."

"That's no problem," Chuck said. "How about I list those as 2a, 2b and 2c, then make timber management your third objective?"

"Good. Thanks so much for the time you've given us this evening, Chuck. It sure was informative. I'll put the pole-light on for you," he added as Chuck went out.

As he closed the door behind Homer and Arlene a few minutes later, he turned back into the kitchen where Tom and Jean were getting on their jackets. "That sure was a lot of information!" Jean exclaimed. "I learned a lot."

"Me, too," Henry yawned. "I'm ready for bed."

# Chapter 7
# Biting the Bullet in the Woods

Two weeks later, Chuck called to arrange a day to mark timber in preparation for the sale. He wanted to start as early as Henry was willing so that he could complete the marking in both Henry's woods and Homer's the same day. They agreed to start at 7:00 a.m the following Monday, if that worked for Homer. Henry asked Chuck if he'd like to come a bit earlier and have breakfast with them.

"That would be great, Henry! How about I plan to get there a bit after 6:00?"

Hanging up the phone, Henry told Rebecca that Chuck would be coming for breakfast the following Monday, and would likely be there for lunch, as well. He couldn't keep the edge of excitement from his voice.

"Are you really looking forward to this timber sale?" Rebecca wanted to know.

"Not really," Henry said, "but I'm eager to get started on managing the woods. This whole thing regarding the future of the farm and doing what needs to be done for the woods has bothered me for several years. Now that I've gotten to know Chuck, I have a much clearer idea of what needs to be done, and I believe he'll see that it is done right."

As usual, Chuck pulled in right on time the following Monday morning. It was overcast, and there was a chance of rain. Henry hoped it would hold off. Rebecca was putting platters of bacon, eggs, and hotcakes on the table as Chuck came in.

"Good morning, Rebecca!" he said with his usual boyish smile. "This sure beats my bagel and cup of coffee on the run."

Conversation was limited as the men concentrated on eating. Rebecca kept their coffee cups filled. Tom came in around 6:30, and joined the table as Chuck and Henry were finishing.

"Will you join us in the woods?" Chuck asked, looking toward Tom.

"No, I figure you've got enough trouble answering Dad's persistent questions," Tom said with a smile. "I've got hay to mow. How long do you figure it will take you to mark the trees?"

"We might be done by noon," Chuck said, "depending on how much Henry wants to discuss which trees we mark for harvest. Once we have that done, it will take me a week to finish working up the data and prepare a request for bids. You'll recall that we want to restrict the cutting to winter months to avoid risk of oak wilt, so there is no great rush. I'd like to get Homer's piece marked this afternoon, however."

"Will you be in for lunch?" Rebecca asked as the men were getting ready to leave. Henry looked to Chuck for the reply.

Catching the question in his glance, Chuck said, "Yes, but would it be okay if we run a bit late? I can't be sure how long this will take, and it would be nice to finish before we come in."

"No problem," Rebecca replied. "I'll keep the soup hot. Don't you be a pest up there, Henry!" Rebecca said, with only a hint of amusement in her eye. "Chuck wants to get that work done this morning."

Chuck pulled an orange vest from back of the seat in his truck and picked up a clipboard. Henry looked with interest at the instruments attached by strings through loops on Chuck's vest, but he didn't inquire about them. They talked little as they walked quickly toward the woods. After they reached the southwest corner of the woods by the creek, Chuck paced away from the creek along the south fenceline for 50 feet.

"We only need to approximate the buffer along the creek," he told Henry. "We don't want to skimp too much, but this is just for protection of the creek. It's not a legal boundary." He pulled out a red flag and hung it prominently on a tree near the fence.

"Ordinarily, we'd paint a red-line by marking trees along the edge of the buffer, to show the logger where logging will stop. In this case, we'll use red flagging so that we don't have to paint trees."

"Will the logger cut the flagged trees?" Henry wanted to know.

"No, boundary trees are not cut," Chuck replied as they walked into the woods. "We'd use a blue-line for property boundaries, although in your case, we may not need to mark property lines. Your north property line has an old fence along it, and I checked with your neighbor who agreed that the fenceline was on the property boundary. We'd ask neighbors to sign an agreement to that effect if there was any question. In this case we will hang some blue flags along the fence just to be sure the logger doesn't mistakenly cross the fenceline. The contract will require that he pull any tops that fall across the line back onto your property. You should discuss the timber sale with your neighbor so that he knows there will be harvesting along there."

He hung another red flag on a six-inch red maple, and proceeded north, paralleling the creek. Twice he went down to the creek and paced up into the woods to make sure he was maintaining at least a 50-foot buffer. When he reached the north fenceline, he hung the last red flag, then walked about 50 feet along the fence and hung a blue flag on the fence. Turning to face south, he pulled out a clinometer and looked through it.

"What is that?" Henry asked.

"It is a combination compass and clinometer," Chuck said. "I want to cover the woods systematically, and will use the compass to keep more or less on north-south lines as we move back and forth across the woods. The clinometer is used to confirm the commercial height of trees where I am uncertain."

"What is commercial height?" Henry wanted to know.

"It is the height of the tree from which logs or pulp sticks can be cut," Chuck answered patiently. "We estimate the number of sixteen-foot logs in trees that are large enough to go for timber, and the number of 100-inch sticks of pulpwood. We won't bother to estimate diameter of pulpwood sticks, but will record species. Roughly, 50-60 sticks will make a cord with the size of wood you'll be selling. When the logger takes pulpwood to the mill, it usually is sold by weight, not volume. We'll have a conversion factor in the contract for converting weight to cords. For timber trees we'll want to note species and diameter so that I can calculate approximate volume. When the logger delivers either sawtimber or pulpwood to the mills, he will get a load slip that will tell us exactly the volume or weight for which you will be paid."

"How can we be sure a logger doesn't take a load and not give us the load slip?" Henry persisted.

"We'll put up a temporary box down near the barnyard in which we will put load tickets," Chuck answered. "On the ticket will be your name and address, and mine, with phone numbers. Drivers are required to have load tickets before entering onto public roads. Mills are good, also, at requiring load tickets before they issue a slip with the volume of the load that is sold to the mill. Loggers would be out of business if they were caught stealing a load. That word would get around quickly. I'm not saying it never happens, but it is rare. Working with a reliable logger with a good reputation is the best way to ensure that you are credited for all wood sold."

Chuck worked quickly, roughly paralleling the red-flagged buffer line they had just established. Pulling a paint-gun of orange paint from his vest, he shook it and walked up to 14-inch red maple. He painted a slash across the truck at about eye level, and another, shorter slash near the ground. Walking around the tree, he painted a second slash at eye level on the opposite side.

"Why the two marks?" Henry asked.

"We don't know from which side the logger might approach a tree," Chuck said, "so this makes it easier for the logger to see trees that are to be cut. The mark near the ground tells us that this tree was selected for cutting. If we find stumps without paint marks, it tells us that the logger took a tree he shouldn't have. We'll put a penalty clause in the contract for cutting unmarked trees, but recognize that occasional unmarked trees may be damaged during felling and skidding. It is a good idea to give the logger a bit of leeway, so that if trees are damaged they can be salvaged. I recommend exercising the penalty only when there is excessive damage and removal of unmarked trees. I generally recommend a 10% leeway. Good loggers rarely would damage more unmarked trees than that. Loggers need to protect their reputations, so they want to minimize damage to residual trees."

As he talked, Chuck was making notations on his clipboard regarding the species, diameter and commercial height of the tree. He handed the paint can to Henry and suggested that he do the marking. Several times Chuck took out his prism and checked basal area. Often he asked Henry which of two or more trees he would prefer to keep. Henry sometimes asked Chuck why he chose a particular tree over another. As the morning went along, they conferred less and less often, and Henry began to be able to pick trees to mark even before Chuck pointed them out. By ten o'clock, they had moved back and forth across the woods several times, and were then working along the ridge line. Each time they reached the north fenceline, Chuck will hang another blue flag on the fence. It was 12:30 when they marked the last tree and headed back for the house.

"I sure learned a lot from that," Henry said as they walked. "This whole thing has been an education for me."

"I'm glad," Chuck responded. "Your interest and involvement sure make my job easier. I'm confident we translated your values and interests in your woods into the marking we just completed. You won't like the timber harvest, I expect. Few people who really love their woods do, but I'm pretty sure you will like the way the woods responds and how it looks in a few years."

After lunch, Henry walked Chuck out. "I'll send you the draft of the request for bids in about a week," Chuck said as he climbed into his truck. "We'll have a good idea of the volume that will be harvested. Once the request is out, we'll need to give timber buyers a month to investigate the sale. Some may want to come out to walk the woods. I expect you'd like them to call and let you know when they're coming," he continued.

"I would," Henry said. "Do potential buyers generally cruise the woods as you've done?"

"Not usually, especially on a small sale like this," Chuck replied. "I don't mean to brag, but most know my reputation, and are willing to accept what I tell them in the request for bids. Maybe none will come out, but especially any new buyers in the area might want to take a look. We're selling on scale, meaning that they pay for what they cut out rather than paying a lump sum. Therefore, they are primarily interested in the quality of the trees and the working conditions in and around the woods."

A week later, Henry received a Request for Bids, marked "DRAFT" in his mail (see Appendix 10). He noted that the volumes were quite close to those originally estimated by the county forester. Henry called Homer to see if he had received the draft and asked if he had reservations or any questions. He didn't, so Henry said he'd let Chuck know that the sale could be advertised.

Chuck said he maintained a list of timber buyers who commonly purchased timber in the area, and he would send the request to them as well as put a notice in the regional newsletter that served the interests of loggers and timber buyers. The newsletter included average stumpage prices for the region, so that buyers and sellers were pretty much aware of price trends. Chuck said that nothing further needed to be done until after the deadline for receipt of bids. As that date approached, he would contact Henry and Homer to arrange a convenient time to open the bids.

It was 6:30 a.m. on the 30th of July when Henry got a call from Chuck saying that he had three bids in hand with two days yet to go before the deadline. He wanted to know if it would be convenient to get together on Monday, the 3rd to open the bids and asked if everyone could meet in Henry's kitchen. Henry offered to contact Homer and see if that would be okay with him, and find out what time would be most convenient.

"That would be fine," Chuck said, "but I have an appointment at 1:00 that day, so I would need to either meet in the morning, or evening. I also need to notify those who have submitted bids in case any want to be present when we open them. It is very seldom that any do, especially on a small sale like this."

"Okay, I'll get back to you as soon as I can contact Homer," Henry replied. He hung up and dialed Homer's number. As expected, he caught him at breakfast. They agreed to meet at Henry's at 7:30 a.m. on the 3rd. Henry let Chuck know.

There was a palatable sense of excitement as they gathered in Rebecca's kitchen. Tom was there, along with Homer and Chuck. Rebecca offered coffee as they were getting seated. Chuck summarized where they were.

Three other bids had come in, making a total of six. Chuck reminded them that they had the right to refuse any or all bids, and that they might want to contact references before making a final decision. He said that they could take a week or so deciding, if they wished.

"What happens if we don't like any of these bids?" Homer asked.

"We can put out another request for bids," Chuck replied, "but I'd recommend waiting a year to do so. It is doubtful we'd attract anything better if we re-bid it immediately. The alternative is to sweeten the offering by increasing the volume of timber and include some of the better trees that were saved."

"I hope that won't be necessary," Henry said. "Personally, I'd take a lower bid if we had to."

"I feel a bit less strongly about it," Homer added, "but like Henry, I want to get this done now."

Chuck opened the bids. Offers for sawtimber ranged from $72 to $105 per thousand board feet (MBF). (Stumpage values vary from sale to sale and week to week, and often by species. These values are given only as illustrations, although they are broadly representative of prices in the Upper Midwest.) Only one bidder offered the same price for both tracts. Each of the others offered a bit more for Homer's sawtimber. Pulpwood prices ranged from $13 to $19 per cord for the hardwood, and $38 to $44 per cord for the pine pulpwood on Henry's plantation. One bidder was not interested in the pine and made an offer only for the hardwood timber.

"Why are they offering more for Homer's wood than mine?" Henry asked.

"I think the primary reason, maybe the only reason, is that we will require the timber on the steep slope by the creek to be cable-skidded. That's much less efficient, and will increase the harvest cost. You'll note that the difference is pretty small, however."

"If I may offer some opinions...." Chuck continued.

"Please do," Henry replied, and Homer nodded his approval.

"I think you should reject the bid from the buyer who isn't interested in the red pines. That would be a difficult sale unless it is lumped with the hardwood sale. I also think the $72 offer for the hardwood timber is too low. I know that buyer, and they use decent loggers, but he's trying to get a bargain, hoping no one else might bid. That leaves four bids. Two of them, in my opinion, are not as reliable and their loggers are more slipshod than I like," he said, pulling two of the letters out of the stack. "One of these has offered the highest bid, but I'd still recommend turning it down."

Henry and Homer indicated agreement with their nods. Henry reached for the other two bids. Homer pulled his chair close so they could look at them together. For the hardwoods, one bid offered $92, and the other $95 MBF. The first offered $15 per cord for the hardwood pulp and the other $15.50. The former offered $42 per cord for the pine pulpwood and the latter $39.75.

Henry asked Chuck if he thought there was much difference between the two buyers and their loggers. Chuck didn't think so. He had worked with both, and had no problems. He thought they were good, honest businessmen and they hired reliable loggers who followed best management practices. He also reminded the men that only certified loggers were to be allowed to work these sales.

"Well, if that's the case," Henry said, "I see no reason why we shouldn't take the higher of the two offers. The difference in their offers for the pine pulpwood is less than we'd get overall by going with the higher bid for the sawtimber." Homer agreed.

"I think that's a good decision," Chuck agreed. "I'll notify Greenwood Lumber that we have accepted their bid, and I'll draw up a contract which the two of you will need to review and sign. We will then get

Greenwood's signature, and you will each get a signed copy of the contract. I'll keep one and one will be returned to Greenwood. I ordinarily ask for a 10% advance, meaning they will pay 10% of the total stumpage expected at the time the contract is signed. We will also ask that they put up a $2,000 performance bond, to be posted before we allow them to start work. I will put this money in an escrow account and hold it until the contract is terminated. The contract will require, as well, that they pay for all wood before it is moved off your properties. They usually do this by sending you a check for a portion of the sale, and then send you additional checks as the amount of wood moved approaches the value of what they have given you. Is this acceptable?"

"Doesn't that mean they always are giving us more money than the timber is worth?" Homer asked.

"Yes, of course," Chuck replied. "As the sale winds down, you will end up with more money than they owe you. Remember that we also hold a performance bond. As we settle up at the end, we may need to refund some of their money. The important thing is that you will always have payment before wood is moved from your land."

Henry and Homer were surprised to hear the rigor of these terms. They wondered if Greenwood would withdraw their offer. Chuck assured them that this was pretty standard practice and was certain there would be no problem. He said he used a standard timber sale contract which included all the state guidelines for timber harvests as well as all these details he had touched upon. He would put a contract for them to look over in the next day's mail. Thanking Rebecca for the coffee, he stood to leave.

"Let me know if any other questions occur to you," he said, "especially as you look over the contract. Congratulations on getting this far. The rest will be pretty routine, although you still have to suffer through the actual logging."

Two days later, Henry received the contract (see Appendix 11) in the mail. That evening he went over it carefully. Several times Rebecca heard him whistle, which she had come to know as an indication of surprise.

"What is it, Henry?" she asked.

"I had no idea how iron-clad a good timber sale contract was, and how firmly it holds timber buyers to rigorous standards," Henry said. "Anyone would be crazy to sell timber without such a contract. This alleviates all the concerns I had about loggers destroying our woods."

"I'm glad you feel that way," Rebecca answered. "I think I'll call the girls this evening to let them know what's happening. They may have some questions that you'll need to answer."

"I'm far less concerned about selling timber now than I was before we got into it." Henry said to Rebecca. "Having a person like Chuck to help makes all the difference."

Henry signed four copies of the contract and drove over to Homer's the next morning for his signature. Homer took an hour to study the contract. Neither of them had any additional questions. Henry mailed the contracts back to Chuck with note saying how pleased he and Homer were with it.

# Chapter 8
# Timber!

On a warm September afternoon, Henry and Tom had just finished unloading the final wagon-load of alfalfa bales when a pickup pulled into the barnyard. "Wonder who that is?" Tom asked, not recognizing the vehicle.

Henry walked over as a neatly dressed man of about 40 stepped out of the truck. "Henry Chapel?" the man asked as he stuck out his hand. "I'm Rick Warren. I handle timber procurement for Greenwood Lumber."

"Glad to meet you, Rick" Henry said. "This is my son, Tom."

Shaking hands with Tom, Rick explained his visit. "Chuck suggested I stop by to meet you when I was in the area. While I'm here, I'd like to take a quick look at the woods. We plan to cut your timber in another few weeks."

"How long do you figure it will take to complete the harvest?" Henry asked.

"If the weather cooperates, we'll be here about a week, then move over to Homer Miller's place. The loggers will cut and pile the wood to be hauled, but it will likely be another week or more before all of it can be moved to the mills. Our aim is to have this sale wrapped up before snow comes."

"That sounds great," Henry said. "Of course you're welcome to go up and look over the woods. You can drive right up there. We have all the gates open up to the woods right now. The yard for piling logs will be in the field to your left as you get to the woods, if that is okay. You'll have to take a section of fence down, of course, or we can do that before you start if you'll give us a few days notice."

"Sure. That won't be a problem. We'd be letting you know when we expect the logger to move in here anyway. Do you have time to ride up there with me?"

"I'd like that," Henry said. "Do you have time to come along, Tom?"

All three men climbed into Rick's pickup. "You must see a lot of this part of the country," Tom said as Rick drove slowly up the lane.

"Sure do," Rick replied with a grin. "We buy timber up to 100 miles from the mill. If we are working with a known consultant like Chuck, I ordinarily don't see the timber until we're about ready to start harvest. But I like to get to know the sellers, and always visit the sale before, during, and after the harvest."

"Why so many visits?" Tom asked.

"The better job our loggers do, the easier my job becomes," Rick replied. "I want to see if there are any likely problems for the harvest before they get here, and I always check on them during the harvest, to be sure they are adhering to the contract, or answer any questions that they or the seller may have. Once harvest is completed, I want to check the site to be sure it was finished and cleaned up the way the contract specifies. If we do a good job, you're more likely to sell timber to us in the future, and you're likely to share your satisfaction with any of your neighbors who may have timber for sale." (See Appendix 12.)

"That makes good business sense," Henry said. "I was reluctant to sell our timber because I had an impression that loggers and timber buyers didn't hesitate to take advantage of sellers and abuse their woods. Chuck sure helped me see that a good consultant and a good contract can make all the difference, but working with the right buyer is also important."

"We hope so," Rick said with a smile. "I think you'll be happy with our logger. His outfit is family-owned, like so many of them. He works with his son and wife. She usually runs the forwarder, he typically runs the feller-buncher, and his son drives the truck, they switch around. We've subcontracted with them for over ten years, and have never had a problem."

They stopped at the gate into the woods, and Tom got out to open it. "We can drive up to the top of the ridge if you want," Henry said as Tom got back in.

At the top of the ridge, Rick turned the truck around before they got out. "I wanted to take a look at this slope," he said pointing toward the creek. "We'll have to fell by hand, and that takes a lot longer than using the feller-buncher. I'm hoping we can do some limbing, then skid the whole tree. We'd then buck out the sawlogs and pulp sticks up here on the ridge, next to the road."

"My only concerns are disturbance to the soil on the slope and damage to residual trees," Henry said.

"Exactly," Rick acknowledged. "We'd want to avoid damage to trees and the soil, anyway, and our contract makes it too costly to do otherwise. We'll not skid anything until the ground is frozen hard or covered with snow. Avoiding damage to residual trees is up to the operator of the skidder. They need to be experienced and patient. I imagine Amy will be doing that while her husband and son do the felling and initial bucking. She's as good an operator as I've seen."

"I've always had the notion that loggers were big, burly men," Tom said.

Rick laughed. "More and more women are working in the forest industry," he said, "and it is very common for family-owned logging firms to involve wives and mothers. We work with one in which a brother and sister and their spouses work together. It's pretty much like farming," Rick continued with a knowing glance at Tom. "Like farming, modern logging involves huge investments in machinery, and considerable skill in operation and maintenance. Profit margins are slim, and hours and working conditions are long and often hard."

They walked along the top of the slope, making a loop back toward the ridge. "This is pretty much as I imagined," Rick said as they walked toward his truck. "It will take as long to get the timber off this slope as it does the rest of the harvest, but we'll do a good job for you. Any questions or special concerns?"

"What about the pines?" Henry wanted to know.

"I glanced over that way as we drove up the lane," Rick said. "I have no concerns about that. It will only take two or three days to complete that harvest. We'll need to take down the fence in a couple of spots, of course. You'll have the cows fenced out of this field, I suppose?" he asked.

"No problem," Henry said. "We'll be ready."

It was snowing when Henry came in for lunch on the last Tuesday of October. No accumulation was expected, and the flurries were widely scattered.

"You got a call from somebody named Rick from Greenwood Lumber," Rebecca said as she set sandwich materials on the kitchen table. "He said the loggers would be in here Thursday or Friday morning, and that if you had any problem or questions to call him anytime on his cell phone. I wrote down his number by the phone. He said you should not hesitate to call in the evening if you needed."

"Don't reckon I need to call him," Henry thought out loud. "Tom and I can go up take down the fence this afternoon or tomorrow. The ground seems frozen hard enough to support their equipment."

On Wednesday evening, Rick called Henry to say that the loggers got held up on their current job and he asked if it would be inconvenient if they didn't start until Saturday or Monday. He told Henry they might drop off equipment the day before.

Friday afternoon, a semi-truck rolled in with the feller-buncher and skidder. Henry came out of the shed where he was changing oil in one of the tractors. "I'm Tony Greeley," the young man said as he stepped from the cab.

"Good to meet you Tony," Henry replied. "I'm Henry. I know your mom's name is Amy. Rick told me about you and your family. What's your dad's name?"

"Andy," came the short reply. Tony wasn't much of a talker, although he seemed friendly enough. Henry could see that he was lean and muscular. His canvas Carhartt jeans were smeared with grease, as was the old baseball cap he wore. An orange label on the hat advertised "Stihl Chainsaws." Henry guessed his age to be about 25. "He'll be along shortly," Tony added. "We plan to start felling timber on the slope tomorrow. Would you prefer that I unload this equipment up at the woods? I can leave the semi parked up there as well, if that would be more out of your way."

"That would be just fine," Henry said. "We've opened the fence to the left just as you get to the woods. The cattle are out of that field, and you have plenty of room to turn around and leave equipment."

"Good enough," Tony replied as he climbed back into the idling truck.

Fifteen minutes later a muddy pick-up pulled in. It had a diesel fuel tank in the back along with an assortment of grease-guns, equipment parts, chainsaws, and several containers of bar oil and fuel mix. "You must be Andy," Henry said as he walked up to the truck. "I'm Henry. Tony has taken the equipment up to the woods to unload. If you'd like to drive on up there, just follow the lane."

"Glad to meet you," Andy responded. "Did Tony tell you that we plan to start the hand-felling tomorrow morning? We'll be here by 7:00 if it's not blowing too hard."

"He mentioned that. You don't need to stop by when you come in, unless you need to pick up some water or anything. We'll still be milking."

"One more thing, then," Andy added. "I expect you'll be curious about what's going on up there while we're working. We sure don't mind you coming up, but we'd appreciate knowing you're there. Trees can do some unexpected things when they are felled, and we need to keep the work area safe. My wife, Amy, will be coming over Monday. She will start on the pines while me and Tony continue felling timber. The feller-buncher is fun to watch if you haven't seen it operate, but keep in mind that the operator can't be looking around all the time for someone who might be near. Please stay well away, and advise anyone else who might like to watch to do the same."

"I appreciate that," Henry said. "I'd like to come by while you're working, and when I do, I'll approach cautiously and let you know as soon as I'm in the area."

"See you tomorrow, then," Andy said.

Henry could hear the equipment being started, then shut down. About an hour later the pickup came out with Tony and Andy. They waved as they drove through the barnyard.

Henry didn't hear them return the following morning, but when he came out of the barn at 7:30, he couldn't help but wince at hearing chainsaws running up in the woods.

"Reckon I'll wander up toward the woods," he said to Rebecca as he finished breakfast. His attempt to sound casual didn't fool her.

"Now don't you go getting in their way, Henry," Rebecca scolded gently. "They know their business."

"Yeah, I agree. They seemed businesslike and pleasant enough when I talked to them last night. They also said I was welcome to check on the work, but was to stay out of the way."

As Henry walked toward the woods, he twice heard the crash of a tree being felled. He cautiously walked along the woods road up the ridge. Soon he could see one of the men down the slope bucking limbs from a large red maple. The other saw seemed near the north property line on the far end of the slope. Henry could see four trees on the ground in the area where the first fellow was working. He decided not to approach, choosing to avoid engaging the man in conversation.

As he watched, the man finished limbing the maple, and moved to the next marked tree. He noticed that the man shut off his saw as he moved, and seemed to study the next tree as he approached. At the base of the tree, the man moved slowly around it, looking up all the while. Having decided how to fell it, he started the saw with an easy motion, pulled down the visor on his helmet, and bent to notch the tree. Henry noted how efficiently the man worked, and how quickly he completed the notch. As he watched, Henry recalled seeing a flock of migratory warblers the previous spring feeding actively in that very tree.

When the chip was out of the notch, the man set the chainbrake, and again studied the tree a few seconds. Apparently satisfied, he moved to the back of the tree and began the felling cut. In less than a minute the large maple began to shake, and Henry watched as the top slowly gained momentum. It slipped through the crowns of three other trees, and landed perfectly, breaking only a single small branch from a nearby tree. Henry could feel the ground shake as the large tree came down.

Henry watched the man fell another tree, then moved to where he could see the other worker. He could tell this was Tony by his build, so clearly, the first worker would have been Andy. Tony worked a bit systematically than his dad, and moved more quickly. He seemed nimble and sure-footed, but spent more time studying trees before felling them. Henry watched as Tony felled two trees. Both came down with minimal disturbance to surrounding trees.

At lunch, Henry described for Rebecca and Tom what he had seen. He thought they might be done felling trees on the slope by Monday. After lunch, Henry again walked up to the ridge and watched for awhile as the two men worked. That evening after dinner, he helped Rebecca clean up.

"You seem quiet, Henry," Rebecca observed. After nearly 50 years of marriage, she could read Henry as well as a cookbook.

Henry gave her a tender smile, but didn't answer right away. After awhile he said, "You remember how depressed you were after Tom was born?"

"Sure. Postpartum depression is not unusual. We didn't know what it was back then, but I felt it again after Beth and Mary were born, although not so much."

"Well, I think I have postpartum depression," Henry said with only a hint of a smile. "I hate the sound of those chainsaws being used up on the ridge by people who haven't seen those trees in the spring when the buds begin to swell and the warblers are feeding in them, and in fall when the leaves are ablaze....people who haven't watched deer and squirrels playing there, or the crows nesting in the big white pine."

"But you know that cutting those trees will make the forest a healthier place and allow the other trees a better chance to grow," Rebecca offered.

"Yes, I know. I'm not sure why, but it is easier for me separate calves for market, or butcher a chicken for dinner. I never minded going up there and cutting a tree for firewood or lumber for the farm, either. I think it is because I've always thought of the woods as a complete entity, sort of like the barn or the farm. I think I would feel the same if some stranger came in here and started tearing boards off the barn, or ripping up one of the fields for some development. They can't know the history, the connection to our family, and the stories we can tell about each piece of this place."

Henry paused, then added, "I wish Tom and me had done the cutting ourselves."

"Henry!" Rebecca scolded gently, "You know you couldn't do all that heavy work in two months, and Tom doesn't have enough time. Besides, it's very dangerous work."

"Yeah, I know. I'm just telling you how I feel. I dread the thought of having those big machines in there even more than the saws, but it will get the work done more quickly and probably with less disturbance when it's all said and done."

"Maybe you shouldn't go up there while the work is going on," Rebecca suggested after a pause. "Let's go to bed, Henry. Some sleep will help. Tomorrow is Sunday, and Mary is coming out in the afternoon."

The following Monday, Tony and Andy continued felling trees on the slope and Amy worked her way through nearly half of the pine plantation with the feller-buncher. Henry couldn't resist going over to watch her work, and found that he didn't feel the same about that as the harvest on the ridge. Mike and Tom walked over late Monday afternoon with Henry. Mike was quite impressed by the big machine, and especially, seeing it being operated by a woman.

Hand-felling was completed Tuesday, and Andy began skidding the trees up the slope to the ridge. Tony worked among the felled trees, setting the chokers. By Wednesday noon, Amy had finished harvesting the pines, and used the forwarder to round up the small piles of eight-foot sticks left by the buncher. They were hauled to the corner of the pasture and stacked neatly in one huge pile that grew by the hour as the work continued. Once the pines were piled, she began moving the hardwood pulp from the ridge where Andy and Tony bucked it out. It was piled next to the pine pulp. Periodically, Amy would bring down a load of sawlogs and piled them in a separate location, opposite the pulpwood, leaving space for the truck to pull between piles for loading.

Henry avoided going up to the ridge. He could hear the snarl and growl of the equipment, however. It fell a bit like having a cavity filled, he told Tom. "I am just hanging on waiting for it to be over."

On Friday, Andy was operating the feller-buncher on the ridge, making quick work of the felling and bucking. Amy continued forwarding the wood to the yard, and Tony began hauling, about ten cords a load, he told Henry as he came out with the first load of pine pulpwood. Work continued through Saturday. On Sunday afternoon, Henry asked Rebecca if she would like to walk up to the ridge and see how close they were to being done.

"Do you really want to see it, Henry?" she asked.

"Not really," he said, "but I need to go up sooner or later, and I'd like to see how much more cutting they have to do."

The forest road that had been so much a part of the forest now was a raw wound winding its way into the heart of the woods. Freshly exposed stumps among randomly tossed branches seemed like stubs left from severed legs on wounded soldiers lying on a battlefield.

Rebecca held Henry's hand, sensing his distress at the sight. They slowly picked their way up the ridge, then down the slope toward the creek. Twice Henry stopped to study where bark had been ripped from near the base of a tree that was unmarked. As they got near the creek, the undisturbed forest received them with intact limbs spread wide like welcoming arms. Neither Henry nor Rebecca said much. Words were not necessary.

On Monday morning, Henry waved down the loggers as they came to work just after 7:00. "How much longer you figure it will take," Henry asked.

"We'll finish tomorrow if we don't have any equipment problems," Andy said. "Amy may need until Wednesday to finish skidding and closing the site, and Tony will be hauling through the rest of the week."

Later that morning, Chuck came in. As he got out of his truck, Henry came out of the barn. "How are you?" Chuck asked by way of greeting. He was a bit more somber than usual, perhaps sensing Henry's distress at the logging.

"It's been a bit hard for me to swallow," Henry said, "but Andy says they'll be out of here before the week's gone."

Chuck acknowledged Henry's comment with a sympathetic nod. "I'm not surprised it's been hard for you, Henry," he said. "I know how much the woods mean to you. I'm going up there to check on the work. Anything you want me to look at in particular?"

"Not really. There's a few trees that have been skinned, but I suppose nothing more than you expected. They are a hard-working team, and good people, I think. Logging is just messy business."

"Yes. It's probably a bit like shoveling manure," Chuck replied. "Once you get used to it, you don't notice the mess so much."

Henry smiled at Chuck's metaphor. "Once the manure is out of the barn, I've got a clean barn," he said. "But once those trees are out of the woods, I've still got the scars to face."

"You're right, of course," Chuck came back. "There's no denying it. Keep in mind that by next fall, the woods will look much better, and the trees will be healthier. It will take four or five years, however, for the wounds to heal."

Two hours later, Chuck stopped on his way back through the barnyard. "Thought I'd tell you what I saw," he spoke to Henry who had come out of the barn when he heard him coming. "They've done a good job. I'd rate their work an A-, based on other logging I've seen. The damage to residual trees is considerably less than allowed, and they have done a great job taking pulpwood out of the tops of the hardwood trees. You'll have plenty of firewood to cut if you want, but their utilization is very good."

"I'm glad to hear that," Henry said. "I haven't seen many logging jobs, and none with this modern equipment like they have."

"Contrary to common thinking," Chuck continued, "having the right equipment reduces the impact of logging. They have better control in felling, and can lift the logs onto the forwarder to minimize skidding damage. The tracks and big tires reduce compaction to the soil. Although there is plenty of disturbance to the surface, it's pretty superficial since the ground is frozen."

Henry nodded, acknowledging Chuck's comments.

"I'll be back Friday to see if they have finished and make sure they close the site as we require in the contract. If they are still hauling, I'll come back next week after that's done. Do you want me to have them close up the fences, or do you want to do that?"

"We'll do it," Henry said. "Ain't seen anyone who can build a fence to suit me."

Chuck smiled, pleased that Henry still had his sense of humor. "I'll see you later this week then," he said. "Give me a call anytime if you have a concern."

# Chapter 9
# Fifteen Years Later

Tom looked out of the barn to see Rusty's well-used pickup coming in the drive. Rusty is Beth's and Randy's older son, Tom's nephew. Although Rusty had grown up in Chicago, summer days on the farm walking the fields and woods with Grandpa Henry, had led to an abiding love for the land. After graduating from high school, he pursued his interest in agriculture at the University of Illinois, where he majored in agronomy. Rusty now lived with his wife, JoAnne, and their two-year old son, Todd Henry, on an adjoining farm which Coon Creek, LLC had purchased ten years earlier. Rusty is junior manager of the LLC and Tom is senior manager. Rusty hoped to buy or be given part or all of his Aunt Mary's and his mother Beth's LLC stock.

"What's the crisis of the day?" Rusty asked with a grin.

"Well, so far, we don't seem to have one," Tom said. He and Rusty had a comfortable working relationship based on respect for each other's knowledge and work ethic. Both knew that when a job had to get done, they could count on one another. "But you can help me finish milking," Tom added.

"No problem," Rusty said, "but I'd like to tap some maples and get ready to make syrup this week, if that's okay with you. The forecast looks good...20s at night and days into the high 30s and low 40s."

"Where you figure to tap?" Tom asked.

"I'd like to keep the taps concentrated so I don't have to spend so much time gathering sap. I thought I'd tap 20 or so of those bigger red maples up on the ridge. They sure have grown well since the timber sale 15 years ago."

"We all will appreciate having the maple syrup," Tom said agreeably. "It also will be good to get some use out of that shelter house and boiler we built last fall. Dad always talked about making maple syrup, but we never seemed to find the time. Hard to believe he's been gone three years," Tom added pensively. "Have you checked out the evaporation pan and buckets you got through eBay?"

"Sure. You recall that we built the boiler so that the pan would fit nicely on it. I'll need to clean all the equipment well, of course. If I can get the taps in this morning, there might be sap to pick up beginning tomorrow," Rusty said with eagerness in his voice.

"Well, I can finish the milking," Tom said, recognizing Rusty's desire to get started. "Why don't you go ahead with the tapping."

After the logging had been completed, Henry looked for the first wildflowers and listened for turkeys for 12 more years. He didn't come home for lunch one April. Tom found him halfway up the hillside above his hemlocks. He was sitting with his back against one of the big oaks, his cane beside him, facing down the slope toward the creek. He'd most likely had a heart attack, the coroner thought. Rebecca said it was the way Henry would have wanted to go, there in the woods overlooking the hemlocks that he loved so much.

Especially on warm spring days, Henry nearly always walked to the woods. Rebecca scolded him not to stress his ailing heart by walking so far, especially up the hill by the creek where he nearly always went.

Henry's response had been, "Each day is a gift, and I like the woods. It's the best place to think. Other than you and the kids, I'd rather keep company with the birds and trees than just about anything I can think of."

As Rusty got close to graduating from college, Tom and Henry asked him to consider coming to the farm. Henry wasn't able to do much after his heart attack , and the work was more than Tom could handle alone. Rusty eagerly accepted their offer, and before he was married he lived for two years with Henry and Rebecca. With Rusty's help and encouragement, Tom expanded the herd and rented the 160 acre farm next door.

Coon Creek LLC also purchased 82 acres from another neighboring farm, and it was in the house on that property where Rusty and JoAnne now lived. Rusty hoped the LLC would be able, in time, to purchase the 160 acres they rented.

Rusty developed a rotational grazing system for the farms that

## MAPLE SYRUP PRODUCTION

If you have maple trees in your forest or around your farm, you might consider making maple syrup as a family project. This is a project that easily involves the entire family. The process as well as the result can enrich family breakfasts, and be shared with neighbors and relatives. If there are enough trees and interest, it can be scaled up to a commercial enterprise to augment farm income. While sugar maple is the traditional species of first choice to tap, red maple, silver maple, and box-elder also provide a sugary sap that can be converted to a tasty syrup (see Appendix 13).

greatly reduced the time required for managing the dairy herd. Because of rotational grazing, Tom and Rusty could take vacations each year. Especially JoAnne, but also Jean, Tom's wife, were much happier with that arrangement. They appreciated being able to get away once in awhile. Because Tom and Rusty could each do the milking alone when necessary, each couple got two weekends a month as work allowed, especially in the winter.

The 160-acre rented farm included 53 acres of woods on the west side of Coon Creek that bordered the family woodlot. As kids visiting the farm, Rusty and his brother Joe waded the creek to sneak into those woods. There was a huge old hemlock on that side of the creek where the turkeys frequently roosted and which he and Joe often climbed. A great-horned owl nested there in late winter, and Rusty could recall climbing up to check out the nest when the owls were not using it.

Henry had never regretted the decision to cut some of the trees. He was proud that he had a good forest management plan and had protected the woods from abusive harvesting. The revenue from the woods allowed Mary to keep her business after her divorce. The vitality of the remaining trees was obvious; they had grown well. He was surprised that the slash and scars from logging faded into the forest so quickly. He and Tom had cut up the larger tops for firewood. Evidence of the harvest was hard to find after only three years. The briars that grew up in the sunnier spots were a nuisance—especially after he had to use a cane, but he noticed that the cover they provided attracted chestnut-sided warblers in the spring, and deer in the winter.

Rebecca grieved Henry's passing so much it worried the family, especially Tom. He more than the others had seen how close his dad and mom were in their golden years. Rebecca, however, carried good memories of her life with Henry. She felt blessed to have all of her children living close. Beth and Randy, Rusty's parents, had built their retirement home on the other side of the ridge, and Beth checked on her mom nearly every day. Mary still operated her store in town; her new husband was retired.

Rebecca was successful in getting Henry away from the farm for their 50<sup>th</sup> wedding anniversary honeymoon in Europe. That was before his heart attack. She and Henry put the farm under a conservation easement before they conveyed it to the LLC. Except for the small lot they sold to Beth and Randy, there would be no more subdivision of the farm. Henry's hemlocks, the towering white pines, and the big white oak like the one against which Henry was seated when he died, would never be cut. All agricultural practices would have to comply with specified conservation standards. Rebecca shared the pride that Tom and Rusty had in the farm, and knew that Henry would also have been proud of the prosperous look of the place. She more than most people appreciated how difficult a farming life can be for families, and was thankful that JoAnne and Jean tolerated the long hours that Rusty and Tom put into the farm work. She and Henry had rarely had a vacation.

Rusty washed the buckets, spiles, and evaporating pan with soapy water, rinsed them with a bit of Clorox in the water, then rinsed them again with clean water. He loaded buckets, a cordless drill with an extra battery, and a bagfull of the spiles into the trailer behind the small John Deere and drove slowly up the lane to the woods. There was still snow in the woods, so he parked the tractor near the gate, and carried the equipment a short distance into the woods. He wanted to tap the closest trees, and also those on the south-facing slope where he thought the sap would run best. If this worked well, he thought he could set up a plastic tube system next year to gather sap into a tank at the gate. Choosing an 18-inch maple with a large, healthy crown, he quickly bored a hole . He blew the wood fragments from the moist hole, then firmly tapped in a spile and hung a bucket. Moving around the tree, he bored a second hole and hung another bucket. In less than an hour, he had tapped 25 trees, and hung 40 buckets. Before he left, several taps were dripping slowly. He spent the rest of the day helping Tom change oil and lubricate the tractors in preparation for the busy season ahead.

The next morning, Rusty had already started milking when Tom came over. They usually traded off doing the feeding and other chores and milking, so Tom let Rusty continue milking while he did the feeding. Together, they could complete milking and chores in less than two hours, but they also were generous in giving each other time off. Working alone, milking and chores took over three hours. Sometimes, Randy would come by to help with feeding.

Tom frequently had breakfast with his mom after chores, and Rusty usually joined them. JoAnne was a school teacher. Rusty was usually gone before she got up, and she would be gone by the time he got through with chores. Beth took care of Todd Henry, her grandson, two days a week. Rebecca liked having him if she wasn't too busy and if Rusty was working around the barns and could help. On other days, JoAnne would drop Todd Henry with a sitter on her way to school.

Tom was 20 years older than Rusty. Tom and Henry had hoped that Tom's son, Mike, would come back to the farm after college, but he never developed much interest in the farm. When Mike's wife was offered a good job in Massachusetts, they didn't hesitate to accept it. They now had two daughters. Rusty was five years younger than Mike, and seemed like a second son to Tom. Jean still worked at the school in town, where her job provided their medical insurance. Rusty also benefited by having insurance through the same school system where JoAnne taught.

"Shall we have breakfast with Mom?" Tom asked, passing through the milking parlor on his way to feed calves.

"Sounds good to me," Rusty said. "Not much point in picking up sap until it warms up enough to dump the sap out of the buckets."

After breakfast, Rusty and Tom drove up to the woods to gather sap. They had a 200-gallon plastic tank strapped into the trailer behind the John Deere. As they checked taps, they emptied sap into five-gallon buckets. Thirty minutes later, they estimated they had collected 25 gallons of sap. Rusty was disappointed that there wasn't more. He knew his evaporating pan would hold about 35 gallons, and that he'd have to boil about 40 to 45 gallons to get a gallon of syrup. Rebecca had offered to finish the syrup on a camp stove on the back porch using a large stainless steel kettle. Boiling would have to wait for another day.

Rusty and Tom had just gotten back to the barnyard when Chuck

drove in. "What are you boys up to?" Chuck asked with his characteristic grin.

"We're getting ready to make maple syrup," Rusty replied with boyish enthusiasm. "I tapped 25 trees up on the ridge yesterday morning,
but we only picked up about 25 gallons of sap this morning."

"They'll start running better in a few days," Chuck assured him.
"You tapped mostly red maples?"

"Yes. I read that red maples make about as good syrup as the sugar
maples do," Rusty said. "Of the 25 trees I tapped, there were only three
hard maples."

"I think you're right," Chuck replied. "You might have to boil longer
to get finished syrup, and that usually means a darker syrup. I know several people who tap mostly red maples, and one fellow even taps box-
elder and silver maples. How's your mom?" he added, turning to Tom.

"She's doing okay," Tom said. "I know she still misses Dad horribly,
however. Go on in and say howdy, if you want. We had breakfast with
her an hour ago."

"I'll do that before I leave," Chuck said. "I stopped by to see if you
guys have given some more thought to setting up your next timber sale.
Now that you've put the forest into a Managed Forest Plan, you're obligated to follow the management plan. You'll recall that we decided to
delay the next harvest while your dad was still living. That first one was
pretty hard for him, and there was no reason to push it while he was still
able to enjoy the woods."

Chuck turned to Rusty with a grin, "Did they teach you anything
about trees at college, or did they just talk about alfalfa and corn?"

"My professors were ag production people. Trees didn't figure on
their farm balance sheets," Rusty replied, "but I like the woods."

"We're considering making an offer for that 160 acres to the west
that we now rent," Tom said. "If we get it, we will have 53 more acres of
woods. It would make sense to hold off a bit and see if we can close that
deal. If so, we'd want to consider a timber sale of our piece plus the new
piece. We know the pine plantation is overdue for a second harvest."

"How soon do you think you'll know about getting the 160 acres?"
Chuck asked.

"Probably before summer. The owner lives downstate. He's never
lived on the place, although he hunted the woods for years. He seems to
have lost interest," Tom said. "He knows we'd like to buy it."

"Give me a call when you're ready to take a look over there," Chuck
said. "Markets for timber aren't real good right now, anyway, and
another year isn't going to make too much difference in your woods,

but the DNR won't let you delay much longer. I'll go say hello to your mom, then be on my way. Good luck with the sugaring."

That evening after dinner, Rusty spent some time on his computer looking into forest management information. "What are you researching," JoAnne asked.

"If we get that other 53 acres of forest, that will give us enough to get serious about managing our timberland," he said. "Grandpa Henry always wished he had more woods, and I think he would have wanted to know more about forest management. I guess I inherited his interest."

"Will getting that other farm mean more work for you?" JoAnne asked a bit anxiously. "I know you love farming, and you're now getting interested in forestry, but don't forget you've got a family too."

The next morning, Rusty picked up 45 gallons of sap. He wasted no time starting to boil it. By 9:00, a great cloud of steam was rolling off the evaporator pan. Rusty was glad to have the cords of firewood stacked under the shed nearby.  Most of it had been cut from fallen and diseased trees during spare time. Rusty enjoyed working in the woods, and he liked using a good wood stove to help heat the old farmhouse where he and JoAnne lived. He figured it was a small return on labor, but since he enjoyed the work, he didn't mind. Also, it helped keep the woods cleaned up and easy to walk through. His thoughts were troubled, however, because he also knew that JoAnne wanted more of his time. He often didn't get home until 7:00 at night, and during planting and harvesting seasons, usually later.

It was near dark and chores were done when Rusty drained the syrup from the evaporator. The two-and-half-gallon kettle Rebecca gave him was nearly full. He carried it carefully to the porch.

"How much you got there?" Rebecca asked. She was especially fond of Rusty, and couldn't help mothering him a bit.

"A bit over two gallons, I reckon," Rusty said. "You want me to turn it on?"

"No, it will keep 'til morning. I'll want to keep a careful eye on it and I don't fancy staying up all night," Rebecca said. She used the same gentle scolding voice that she had used with Henry. Rusty recognized it as her way.

The next morning Rusty was in the kitchen when Rebecca came out. "You're awfully early today," she said with her gentle smile.

"I thought I'd start the sap boiling," Rusty said. "The kettle is just starting to boil. I expect to have another batch to boil off today or tomorrow."

"I'll look after this batch," Rebecca said. "I have a candy thermometer to tell when it is done, but that won't likely be until sometime this afternoon. I read somewhere that a boiling temperature of 220° would indicate that the proper sugar concentration had been reached."

"Can we check it now," Rusty asked.

"Sure, honey." She handed Rusty the thermometer. It registered 215°.

"I don't know that there is any particular reason is has to be more concentrated," Rebecca said, "except it is a bit thin at this point. Have you tasted it?" she asked, handing Rusty a spoon.

"It's really sweet!" Rusty said, handing the spoon back. "And good!"

"Why don't we keep boiling it. When you come in for lunch, we can check it again."

Rusty hastened out to catch up with Tom who was already well into chores and milking. "How's the syrup," Tom asked as Rusty came into the barn.

"Boiling. Grandma thinks it should boil until at least noon to get a bit thicker."

"I'll help you pick up sap after breakfast," Tom offered. You'll probably need to boil again tomorrow, I suppose."

At noon the sap registered 219° on the candy thermometer. Rebecca said she could can it in quart jars without any help. Rusty reported that they had another 45-gallon morning, and that he would be boiling a second batch the next day.

A week later, Rusty and Rebecca, with some help from Tom and a bit of help from Randy gathering syrup and feeding the boiler, had produced five gallons of finished syrup. They were all pleased with their first effort at making maple syrup. Rebecca announced that there would be a big pancake breakfast for everyone on Easter morning. Tom offered to bring the sausage they had made last winter with venison and pork

from the hog they taken to the slaughter house in September.

At breakfast on Easter Sunday, Rebecca asked for everyone's attention. "It was just about three years ago that Henry died," she said. "You all know how much he loved this place and his family. I feel that he's with us this morning, sharing in yet another fruit of his beloved woods. It seems that Rusty has continued Henry's love affair with the woods. That makes me so happy, and I know that Henry is equally pleased. And," she went on, "I am so happy to have you all here this morning. Please forgive my tears."

Tom slipped his arm around this mom's sagging shoulders and gave her a hug.

"Well, maybe this is a good time to make my announcement," Rusty said. "I plan to begin taking a series of short-courses on forest management that the state Extension forester coordinates. They meet for four different weekends at locations around the state."

Before others could speak, Grandma Rebecca clinched it for Rusty. "Henry would have liked that."

"I've agreed to cover for Rusty those weekends," Tom offered, "but it is JoAnne's support you really need.

"We've talked about it," JoAnne said with a smile. "I'm happy that Rusty is getting excited about forest management. I know his interest goes back to his early days walking in the woods with Grandpa Henry. We've decided that our next vacation will be to Europe, and be a second honeymoon. Rusty thought he might see if we could connect with a forestry tour the state university conducts over there each year.

"And I've agreed to take Todd Henry while Rusty and JoAnne are in Europe ," Beth added. "Well I hope I get a bit of time with Todd Henry also," Rebecca added. "With a little guidance I think he may become another chip off the Henry Chapel block, and that is a pretty sound piece of wood."

Appendices

# APPENDIX 1

# QUESTIONS TO ASK A PROFESSIONAL FORESTER

1. If left uncared for, how would our woods change over the next 50 to 100 years? Are our woods healthy now? What would make them healthier?

2. Given our priorities for our woods, how can we enhance the benefits?

3. Are there current or potential problems with insects or disease in our woods that should be addressed?

4. Are there invasive species in our woods or neighborhood that either now or will likely create a problem maintaining the benefits we desire from our woods?

5. Are there certain species of trees that should be reduced, and some that might enhance our woods? If so, how could this adjustment be achieved?

6. If management is done, what would it likely cost us, or what financial return might result? What does it cost to do the things we'd like to do? Will there be a financial return for our efforts and what will it be?

7. If a timber sale is suggested, what control do we have over who does it, how it is done, and when it is done? If we need to remove some trees, how do we get someone we can trust to do it so that we are happy with the results.

8. How can we find a consulting forester that we can trust and who has our best interest in mind? Can we see examples of their work or talk with others with whom they have consulted?

9. Are there neighbors who have similar forest management goals and needs?

10. Is there technical or financial assistance that the government provides? How do we apply?

# APPENDIX 2
# PLANTATION MANAGEMENT

Conifers are most widely used for reforestation, but depending on the landowners objectives and the site, hardwoods can also be considered. Conifers are easier to plant, and require less management than hardwood species. Hardwoods are more often direct-seeded.

Competition from undesirable vegetation is the greatest obstacle to establishment of trees. Conifers more quickly control undesirable competition than hardwoods, so more mechanical or herbicide use is generally necessary with the latter. In nearly all new plantations, some herbicide application is usually necessary. Check with your Extension of natural resource office to get recommendations for your conditions.

Conifers are generally planted in rows 8 to 10 feet apart, with trees 6 to 8 feet apart in the row. If you space rows 8 feet and trees 6 feet (two paces) in rows, you will have planted about 900 trees per acre (8 x 6 = 48 square feet, divided into 43,560 square feet per acre = 908 trees/acre). Ideally, survival should be about 800 trees per acre. At this spacing, you will not need to thin the trees until they can be sold for pulpwood. Hardwoods are often planted somewhat farther apart.

Competition from grass or forbs (broad-leaved herbaceous plants) or woody shrubs is a common cause for poor establishment. Mowing with a brush-hog, or root-raking with a dozer is desirable before planting if woody vegetation is well established on the site. Pre-planting site treatment with herbicides often leads to better success. Site preparation can be done in late summer or spring before you plant depending on species and conditions. A consulting forester or natural resource professional can prepare a plan and advise you on questions concerning site preparation and herbicides.

The species you plant, the size of area to be planted, and the type of terrain will largely dictate whether you can machine plant or plant by hand. Very steep or rocky ground may prevent use of machine planting, but keep in mind that extreme conditions may also prevent forest management, even harvesting. Such marginal sites should be used to promote diversity or wildlife. A person can plant about half an acre, or 500 small conifer trees per day by hand. Hardwood seedlings require about twice as long to plant. Three people, using a single row planting machine in a well-prepared site can plant five acres (5000 conifer trees) a day. Planting machines can often be rented at a nominal cost from state natural resource agencies, although you will have to provide a tractor to pull it.

When planting by hand, especially in sod, a single bottom plow is particularly useful for site preparation. The shallow furrows create weed-free, water-retaining rows laid out on the contour, or if the field is nearly level, furrows can run straight. Furrows can be done in the autumn before the ground freezes, or just ahead of planting. Furrows generally prevent the necessity for pre-planting herbicide application, however, some people do not like having trees in rows or old furrows that will persist for dozens of years. About the only alternative to using a plow in sod is either use of herbicides or grubbing off a sod-free area of approximately a square foot in which to plant each tree. The latter will double or triple the planting time.

Planted trees will grow slowly for the first year or two, but usually begin rapid growth by their third year. As tree crowns begin to close, competition from other plants will be largely eliminated, especially with conifers. This usually occurs in less than 15 years on good sites. As canopy closes you should consider thinning to maintain good growth. With hardwood plantations, you probably will not need to thin for 20 years or more after planting. You may want a forester to advise you on when to thin, and for help with a timber sale contract. First thinning is often done by removal of every third row in conifers. This process, although taking some dominant trees, allows for efficient machine operation. Second thinning will depend on growth rates and should follow the recommendation in your forest management plan. Thinning in hardwoods generally involves removal of inferior trees which often are too small to sell.

After the first thinning, you may want to consider pruning. Removing lower limbs will allow the trees to produce clear wood, although it does not increase growth rate. In conifers, the limbs removed usually are only dead ones. In hardwoods, pruning requires more knowledge. How-to-prune references are readily available in libraries or online. Clear wood is an advantage only on trees that will be grown for saw-logs. If economics is your motivation, prune only the very best trees. As they get bigger, you can prune higher, up to about 17 feet, but always maintain at least 1/4 live crown. The economic benefit of pruning conifers is marginal, at best, but some do it because they prefer the appearance.

Plantation may also need protection from deer or rabbits. Browsing can be a very serious problems with species such as northern white-cedar or hemlock, and with most hardwoods. Tree shelters or fencing is commonly necessary with any hardwood, but especially with oaks.

The species you choose will be determined, in part, by your goals. If you simply want tree cover on the land, you might choose faster growing species, or species that provide the best wildlife habitat. If you want to market some or all of your plantation as it matures, you should choose species that will have the best market value. Most people will have multiple goals, and will choose species that provide multiple benefits, not necessarily optimal for any one. Either way, well planned plantations, like landscaping around your home, provide many benefits, including increased value of your land.

# APPENDIX 3

# PLANTING PRACTICE

Seedlings are usually available from state nurseries at cost, although many private nurseries also sell tree seedlings. Planting is nearly always done in the spring, and should be scheduled as soon after ground thaws as possible. Site preparation,should be done before planting to reduce weed control afterwards, but follow-up is generally necessary regardless. When ordering conifer seedlings, figure on 1000 per acre. Hardwood seedlings are generally spaced wider. Determine the number you need by multiplying the space between rows times space between seedlings. Divide this product into 43,500 square feet per acre. For example: rows 10 feet apart with seedlings 8 feet apart in rows equals 80 square feet per tree or 545 trees per acre. Seedlings for reforestation are usually sold in units of 100 or 1000, and are bare-root. Depending on species, seedlings are typically two or three years old. The larger, and more expensive seedlings will have larger roots and require more work to plant, although once established, they will grow more quickly the next couple of years.

From state nurseries, you can generally select either graded or straight-run conifer seedlings. Graded seedlings have been sorted so that you get consistent stock, but they will be more expensive, whereas straight-run will include many small seedlings, some of which should be thrown away. The number of seedlings in straight-run bundles is nearly always more than is specified, so you can cull generously and still have enough to meet your needs.

Seedlings are lifted from the nursery as soon as the ground thaws, and are shipped or made available soon after. Seedlings should be planted as quickly as possible after lifting from the nursery, ideally within 48 hours. If a delay is necessary, trees should be kept cool (34-38 degrees is optimal), in shade, and moist. Do not plan to hold seedlings more than a few days, at most. Sprinkle the seedlings to maintain moisture; DO NOT soak them in water. If longer delay is necessary, bundles should be opened to avoid overheating, however, the longer you delay planting, the greater the mortality.

When you are ready to plant, root-prune the seedlings if they have long, straggly roots. This may seem illogical, but it is new root growth that provides most water absorption in plants, and pruning not only stimulates new root development, but also avoids long roots getting balled into ineffective masses in the planting hole. This is an especially important step for conifers. It may not be necessary for hardwoods, whose roots will likely have been cut when they were lifted. Taking small bunches at a time, straighten out roots over a wood block, and use a sharp hatchet or axe to cut off the longer roots, leaving the larger, stronger roots. This can generally be done with three or four quick chops. Immediately afterwards, place the seedlings in a bucket of water and plant as quickly as possible. Avoid allowing seedlings to stand in water for more than an hour.

A spade or dibble is the best tool for hand planting. Examine a seedling and note the soil line at the top of the root crown. You will want to plant the seedling at this same depth. It is especially important to prevent roots from drying. On dry, windy days you may need to prune and plant only a few dozen trees in a batch, so that each is placed in the ground quickly.

With the spade or dibble, open a trench slight deeper than the length of the root mass. Holding the stem near the top of the root crown, push the roots into the slit and by moving the seedling down then slightly back up to the proper depth, roots will be generally be positioned properly. If not, repeat the motion until roots are in the slit, and appear to spread toward the bottom. Avoid using the spade or dibble to insert the seedling as this will likely damage the roots.

Once the seedling is at the proper depth, insert the spade of dibble two or three inches from the seedling, and by pulling the handle away, the soil can be pressed against the roots of the seedling (see illustration). Push the dibble toward the seedling to firm the soil against the upper part of the roots. Using your heel, the hole made by the dibble is pressed close as the final step. Once you get the hang of it, this process can be completed in less than 30 seconds.

When planting larger seedlings or hardwoods, a shovel often is necessary. Dig a hole about the size of the root ball, and slightly deeper. Center the root ball in the hole, and loosely replace soil in and around roots. Fill the hole with water to settle the soil, adding more soil as necessary, to make a slight mound around the tree. Use your toe to carefully press the soil down leaving a slight depression.

If you are lucky, there will be no prolonged hot, dry weather especially the first month or two after planting. If there is, you may need to water your trees, although this is feasible only with small plantations. Generally, trees are planted at a density assuming some mortality. If proper site preparation is done, and care is taken during planting with follow-up weed control, tree survival is usually good. Within two or three years, trees should be well enough established that no further weed control will be required, although watch for invasive species, or woody shrubs that can grow quickly from roots that remained in the ground after initial site preparation.

# APPENDIX 4
# FOREST-PROPERTY TAX BREAKS

Tax deferment programs for forested acreage usually require a stewardship plan approved by a state forester. Under a contract with the state, certain practices are mandatory and others are optional. While the plan should address your priorities for your forest, generally mature trees must be harvested according to a timetable. Some states now do not require severance tax for a required harvest during the first few years after entering into tax deferment program.

Some forest owners may not wish to cut timber from their forest, even if mature trees are present. If so, because of variation in the requirement among states, it still is worth checking with your state natural resource agency. Keep in mind, however, that the primary reason favorable woodland tax policies have been developed is to keep raw material flowing to the mills. Property tax benefits to forest owners must be offset by proportionately greater tax burden on other property. These programs have been approved because public officials recognize the many benefits that derive from good forest management and the economic multiplier effect of pumping round wood into processing and manufacturing mills.

Reduction or deferral of property taxes can be a substantial benefit, and may be essential, or at least an important incentive for you to keep your forested property. In any case, a management plan is a good idea. However, the long term contract (10-50 years) may reduce the potential sale price of the property because the contract goes with the property and continues to regulate the activities of any new owner unless a an often substantial penalty is paid to get out of the contract. Placement of buildings on the land or selling hunting leases may be prohibited. In some states, owners may be required to permit public access for recreation or hunting. Check your local policies for specific regulations.

# APPENDIX 5

# WAYS TO TRANSFER WOODLAND PROPERTY TO HEIRS

Limited Liability Corporations (LLC) have become a popular mechanism to transfer property of substantial value that typically generates an annual cash flow (farms and small businesses—especially by professionals that want to limit personal liability). A woodland owner can also hire an attorney to create a LLC, issue stock and transfer the ownership of the property to the corporation. Part or all of the shares can be given in equal or unequal number to children, grandchildren or any other party. The shares can be sold or willed to future generations as long as the LLC exists. Shareholders meet annually to make major decisions, select a manager, and adopt a budget. LLCs provide a lot of flexibility and an unlimited time horizon.

However, an LLC may not be appropriate to transfer woodlands that do not generate a regular cash flow. Without a cash flow, the shareholders would be forced to levy annual assessments on themselves to pay for property taxes, tree planting, pest control, access maintenance, fencing etc. Annual cash assessments (and rare dividends) plus the organizational costs of initial attorney fees, continuing record keeping, annual reports and annual meetings, can turn an exciting idea into a "drag" and potentially into a conflict between shareholders who cherish the property and those who want to liquidate it.

Other options may solve some of these problems. Suggestions follow, but it would be prudent to consult an attorney before selecting one.

**Transfer to a single heir:** The traditional method of transferring rural land was to just deed it or will it to the oldest son. (Interestingly in the small Himalayan country of Bhutan, the eldest daughter gets the farm.) In more recent times the farm and associated woodland went to the child (usually son) who stayed home to work the land and take care of the parents. With the most "sweat equity", the highest emotional attachment to the land and responsibility for the parents, the other siblings usually found the arrangement more or less fair.

However, the practice has become more contentious as the value of real estate has sky rocketed which means that the "favorite child" who stayed home stood to get very significant financial assets and the siblings would get little or nothing because most of the parent's assets were in the farm.

**Transfer to a single heir while giving life-estate rights to other heirs:** In this scenario the simplicity of a property transfer to a single heir is combined with a transfer of some temporary property rights to other heirs (siblings, grandchildren, non-relatives). This mechanism allows one or two generations of other family members to have emotional, physical and legal attachment to the property but no financial or managerial involvement. As each of the named life estate holders dies, their rights are extinguished.

The most common use of life estates involve retention of the right to live on the property or use the property in some other way by the owner after the property is deeded to a new owner. However, the seller can also reserve certain rights and give those rights to a third party(s) – rights such as to use a cabin, to hunt, to pick berries, to meditate, etc. For example, if the property is given or sold to one child, guaranteeing that the other siblings and their children could continue to hunt on the family woodlot for their lifetimes would go a long way to maintaining positive family relationships.

**Transfer to a partnership:** Partnerships involve a formal arrangement between two or more individuals or corporations. Larger partnerships typically have an executive management structure. Partnerships can be a mutually rewarding experience when the goals and ethics of the partners jive and there is a clear division of labor. All partners might be active in the business, some might be passive except for certain major decisions and, in still other arrangements, some partners may be silent with only a financial relationship.

Partnership agreements should include provisions to dissolve the partnership and provisions to deal with the death of a partner. Provisions include right of survival language or a buy/sell agreement with a paid-up life insurance policy to pay off the heirs of the deceased partner.

**Transfer to two or more heirs as tenants-in-common owners:** All tenants-in-common owners must agree on the management or sale of the woodland. However, if one of the heirs wants to sell his interest in the property, he is free to do so. A sale to an outsider is unlikely since the buyer would have no affirmative ownership prerogatives and could only veto decisions. More importantly, when a tenant-in-common dies, his property interest is transferred to as many heirs as are named in his will or as are designated by probate court if a will does not exist.

Some families want to keep all their descendants in the ownership circle of the family forest by encouraging their heirs to name all their children as tenants-in-common through succeeding generations. Thus, the number of owners can multiple and involve individuals with little relationship to the family forest. Management decisions about the land can become more and more cumbersome. Payment of property taxes and other expenses can become contentious. One or more owners might even go to court to force a liquidation sale of the property to cash out their fractional interest. Accordingly, transfer to tenants-in-common is not recommended.

**Transfer to two or more heirs in joint tenancy with rights of survivorship:** In contrast to the previous mechanism, transfers to joint tenants with rights of survivorship re-concentrates ownership. As the original heirs die, the other heirs assume their property rights. Of course, any joint tenant can sell or give his right to another joint tenant. However, sale of all or any property rights and any major management decisions, like harvesting trees, require consent of all joint owners. The joint tenant that out lives all other joint tenants gets a sole ownership deed with no restrictions as to sale or transfer on death.

**Transfer to two or more heirs as joint tenants with rights of survivorship with the creation of a Property Retention Trust:** If the primary objective of the transfer is to keep the property whole and keep it in the family (equity between heirs is not paramount), a Trust can be created to facilitate long term ownership of the entire woodlot by at least one member of the family. The Trust document must clearly spell out who will be the original heirs (owners as joint tenants) and who could have future ownership possibilities under the terms of the Trust. The Trust might also structure the method of making decisions within the context of the Trust to allow decision-making on some issues without unanimous consent of all joint tenants.

**A Property Retention Trust** is intended to focus ownership of the property in one or a small number of family members under the assumption that long term tender loving care is best achieved by individuals with a high degree of attachment to the land and possibly residency on the property. That objective is met by naming a select group of heirs as joint tenants with rights of survivorship. With rights of survivorship, the number of owners will automatically decreases as joint tenants die. Thus it may be desirable to include grandchildren, and possibly even a special friend of the family, in the list of heirs. With longer life expectancies, grandchildren are likely to be adults by the time mother and dad pass. Hopefully, a grandchild(s) will have developed an appreciation for the family forest. A grandchild or an in-law or a special family friend (many woodland owners have no children or no children with any interest in the woods) may be the only person with strong interest in this living family legacy. If at least one grandchild is still a minor, it will be difficult to sell any part of the property because the minor can not sign away their interest—which is desirable if the owner wants the grandchildren to have the opportunity to eventually own the property.

The ownership may funnel down to one joint tenant before all the other joint tenants die if all the other joint tenants decide to transfer their undivided fraction interests to one of the joint tenants. Or all the joint tenants could decide to transfer the property to someone else. By reducing the cost of owning the woodland, the Property Retention Trust Fund is designed to encourage a family member to be the recipient of that transfer – to consider taking on the responsibility of owning the property.

Initially, there would be one-time legal fees to create the Trust; it would then be dormant until funded—probably with assets available at the time of death of the owner(capital gains taxes exempt) of the owner. The owner has the option of transferring the property to the joint tenants and depositing assets in the Trust Fund prior to death. Income from the Trust Fund could pay property taxes and possibly other property maintenance costs such as surveying, fencing and roads/trails/bridges at any time after it was created.

The Trust Fund can be structured to reduce the temptation of the joint tenants to sell the property to an outsider because the substantial assets in the Trust Fund would be not be accessible to the joint tenants and would be lost to the family if such a sale occurred. However, a family member could pay the other joint owners a premium for the property because the costs of owning the property would be dramatically reduced. The Trust Fund would continue indefinitely as long as someone, referenced in the Trust document (such as future descendants, in-laws or designated family friends), owned the land. If the property is sold to someone not referenced, the Trust would be terminated, with the assets in the Trust Fund directed to a charity – possibly the Land Trust that holds and enforces the Conservation Easement (if any) on the property.

# APPENDIX 6
# CONSERVATION EASEMENTS

Under a conservation easement you give some property rights to a governmental agency, or more commonly, to a private Land Trust. The Land Trust is typically organized by citizens in your part of the state for the purpose of accepting and enforcing conservation easements. You usually give up development rights – the right to subdivide your property for residences or commercial purposes. Billboards, commercial facilities, industrial uses, mining, waste disposal and major landscape alterations also are commonly prohibited. If you choose, you can retain the right to a limited number of land title divisions, or to build a limited number of buildings. If too many rights are reserved, however, conservation values may be compromised and the Land Trust may not be interested in protecting the property.

A conservation easement specifies which activities are allowed or prohibited on the property. For instance, you might wish to specify that trees of a certain size or a certain species are to be protected (like Henry's hemlocks and large oaks). One might choose to protect old stone fences, or prevent alteration of natural features such as wetlands. Too many details, however, make monitoring burdensome to the Trust that will monitor and enforce the easement. It is important, nevertheless, for the landowner to give a sense in the easement of those values they wish to preserve in perpetuity.

The landowner has a complete range of options, and the process is completely voluntary. Once the landowner and Land Trust agree on the terms of the easement, the landowner executes a formal document to transfer specific property rights to the Land Trust. The document is recorded in the Courthouse and becomes part of the deed to the property.

You and all subsequent landowners are legally bound to comply with terms of the easement. The Land Trust agrees to inspect the property periodically and to take legal action if necessary to enforce compliance. Thus, you can be confident that future landowners will not mistreat the property, or develop it. Land Trusts usually ask for a donation to their endowment to cover future costs of monitoring, and if necessary, court costs to enforce terms of the easement. There also will be costs for an appraisal and legal fees, plus filing costs at the Courthouse.

Granting an easement will typically reduce the value of the property. That loss in value may qualify as a gift to a non-profit organization (the

Land Trust) and an income tax deduction. Estate taxes and property taxes also are often reduced, reflecting the lower value of the property.

In addition to the tax benefits of a conservation easement, each time the landowner walks through the meadows or woods, the experience is more serene knowing that the land has been protected. Forever!

# APPENDIX 7
# HIRING A CONSULTING FORESTER

Few of us would seek professional help from just any doctor or any lawyer, or even just any mechanic to fix our car. If we need professional help, we often will at least look for someone with a good reputation and who has pertinent experience and training. Forest management is every bit as complicated as any biological, legal, or mechanical problem you are likely to incur. Indeed, forest management involves all three paradigms. Professional foresters have four-year college degrees from accredited forestry schools. Additionally, consulting foresters usually have several years of experience gained by working under the guidance of more experienced foresters. Where and how can you find the right one?

Contact your state natural resource agency and ask for a list of consulting foresters serving your area. In most states, there will be a local or regional natural resource office near you, and you can find them listed in the Yellow Pages. If you have neighbors that have used consulting foresters, ask them for names and recommendations. You may also want to begin your forest management planning with a visit from a state or county forester serving in your area. They can provide you a list of consulting foresters to follow up.

Do not feel obligated to hire anyone in particular. Interview them as you would any prospective employee. Think about what is important to you about your forest and prepare a list of questions to determine their responses. It is especially important that the consulting forester you hire be sensitive to your goals and values. If they disagree with any, they are obligated to explain why to your satisfaction. If you do not feel they can work with you to achieve your goals and values, or fail to convince you to consider alternatives, look farther. There are plenty of good consulting foresters, and you need only one.

# APPENDIX 8
# AESTHETICS: MANAGING FOR NATURAL BEAUTY

Natural beauty and wildlife consistently rank at the top of landowners' list of values they seek from their woods. When asked what constitutes a beautiful woods, the responses are again remarkably consistent: big trees, diversity of species/sizes/colors, unusual specimens, and a broad landscape view of forest edges provided by small fields, open wetlands, or lakes.

These values can be protected (and even enhanced) by a careful commercial harvest that leaves the largest trees, den trees, trees with unusual shapes, and species uncommon in the forest. Competing, prolific species can be harvested more intensely.

However, there are many ways to maintain and enhance natural beauty that do not involve commercial harvesting:

1. Small groupings of especially attractive species (pines/birch/oaks that hold their bronze leaves through the winter) can be planted in openings in the woods or along the forest edges.

2. Forest edge can be micro-managed to enhance aesthetic pleasure. A landowner should note which trees and combinations of trees along roadways and trails are especially attractive in every season. In spring different species bud out with different colored leaves and flowers: nile-green aspen, maroon birch, yellow willow, purple maple, red oak, white-flowered cherries and plums. In summer all plants are working hard in monotonous green overalls. Autumn is a treat to the eyes wherever deciduous trees grow, but a mix of species heighten the treat and make it last longer. Winter is also visually interesting if the forest edge contains conifers, red dogwood, trees that hold their leaves, and trees whose size and form attract attention. White birch and to a lesser extent aspen, lighten and stand out on the forest edge in every season.

Painting such a landscape requires many small brush strokes with a chain saw over many years. Selection of which trees to thin out should be made from the point of viewing—not next to the tree. The cut trees can be used for firewood or left to recycle their nutrients.

3. Private forest roads and smaller trails can be moved to take advantage of the best scenery—the most interesting topography (ridges, depression, streams), the most interesting trees (large, deformed, rare), and the most likely place to see wildlife (dead trees, den trees, thickets). A trail that curves, follows the contour, and encounters obstacles such as fallen logs or low hanging branches give the human brain both an aesthetic high through the eyes and a kinesthetic high through variable muscle movements.

# APPENDIX 9
# FOREST MANAGEMENT PLAN

DRAFT

Forest Management Plan
Henry Chapel and Family
12 April 2012

This management plan applies to two forested tracts on the Henry Chapel farm, located on Coon Creek Road, Harrison Township, Tuscarora County, Wisconsin. One tract, hereafter called the "Plantation," consists of 12 acres of 45-year-old, unthinned red pine. The second tract, hereafter called the "Woods," consists of 35 acres of unmanaged mixed hardwoods. Both tracts border the east side of Coon Creek (see map).

Henry Chapel and his family have a great interest in the woods which he and his wife, Rebecca, have owned for 46 years. It is their expectation that the property will remain in the family for the foreseeable future, and they plan to place a conservation easement on the entire farm, including the forested tracts. Their priorities for management (listed more or less in order) are:

1. Health of the forest (including wildlife and all native species).
2a. Aesthetics
2b. Recreation (hiking, nature study, hunting)
2c. Firewood and maple syrup production
3. Timber production, for personal use or sale

Plantation

2-0 red pines were planted on 12 acres of poor pasture land, along the west side of the Chapel farm in 1965. Soil is Markey sandy-loam on 3-7 per cent slope. Previous farming practices resulted in loss of much of the topsoil, leaving 2-3 inches of A horizon, over a deep (>30 inches) B horizon with no restriction on infiltration within the surface three feet. This is an excellent site for red pine, with no special management required.

Pines were planted on a 6' x 6' spacing (1210 trees per acre). Canopy closure occurred at approximately 15 years of age. Average height of trees is now 50 feet. Some mortality (<10%) has occurred, primarily because of crowding. Interior trees have less than 20% live crown (10 foot).

Stand Objective. To protect stream margin from erosion and optimize timber production.

Recommendation. Thinning is urgently required. Because this area is not exposed to extreme wind, soil is deep and trees have well developed roots, and because snow-loading is not a serious problem, the first thinning should be removal of every third row, or approximately 400 trees per acre. Non-commercial stems should be dropped and left on the ground unless the owner wants to remove them for his own use (not recommended for indoor fuel). Estimated yield will be about 20 cords per acre, with utilization down to 3-inch diameter, or 16 cords down to 4 inch diameter. Thinning can occur any time when ground will support equipment without rutting.

The plantation should be evaluated 10 years after thinning for consideration of a second thinning. Trees will be approaching 70 feet tall, with average diameters of 8-10 inch d.b.h. (range 5 to 14 inches d.b.h.). In the second thinning, approximately another third of the stems should be removed in a selection harvest during which crop trees are left. Generally, the smallest diameter stems should be removed and the largest left as crop trees.

Woods

This 35-acre forest extends from Coon Creek up a west-facing slope (10-20 per cent) to a ridge that rolls off to the east and southeast. Soil along the creek is a Markey silt loam (3-6 per cent slope), giving way to Scott sandy-clay-loam on the slope (10-20 per cent slope), and a Scott sandy loam on the ridge (0-6 per cent slope). These are excellent soils for mixed hardwoods. The forest has had individual trees removed over time, although there is no evidence of an overall harvest. Owners have removed down and dead trees, primarily for firewood. Pit and mound microtopography suggests historic wind-throw, probably of large white pines, although no recent wind-throw is evident.

Habitat type along Cook Creek, on the Markey silt loam, is mesic northern hardwoods. The slope and ridge is a dry-mesic habitat. A buffer will be maintained along the creek that encompasses most of the Markey soil type. Differences in composition and growth rates of the trees on the slope are not appreciably different from those on the ridge, so I recommend the remainder of the Woods be managed as a single unit.

The dry-mesic habitat type has good to very good capability for timber production. There are no exotic or invasive species present at this time, although the woods should be checked annually for presence of invasives. The site has no known archaeological/historical structures, nor threatened or endangered species.

Table. Approximate composition of the Woods, in April 2012, prior to any management. Data are basal area per acre based on 40 prism samples spaced systematically throughout the slope and ridge (excluding a 50-foot buffer along Coon Creek).

| Species | Basal area (ft$^2$/ acre) |
|---|---|
| Basswood | 2.4 |
| Black oak* | 7.4 |
| Eastern hemlock | 3.6 |
| Eastern hophornbeam | 5.0 |
| Eastern white pine | 20.5 |
| Northern red oak | 18.7 |
| Paper birch | 8.9 |
| Red maple | 27.0 |
| Sugar maple | 12.3 |
| White ash | 10.4 |
| White oak | 22.1 |
| Total | 138.3 |

*Includes *Quercus velutina* and *Q. ellipsoidalis* (northern pin oak)

Trees range in size up to 28 inch d.b.h. (eastern white pine), although most trees are < 18 inches d.b.h. While over-stocked, this forest appears to be in good health with reasonable vigor. Reproduction is minimal. No obvious disease or insect problems are present.

Understory shrubs and small trees include serviceberry (Amelanchier spp.), eastern hophornbeam, hornbeam (mostly, on lower slope), and small red and sugar maple. One 16-inch butternut was found along Coon Creek in the buffer zone. It was diseased (canker). Nearly all hemlock are within the buffer zone, although three were sampled near the bottom of the slope.

Stand Objective. Maintain diversity, health and vigor of the stand.

Recommendations. A 50-foot buffer should be left along Coon Creek with no disturbance. The remainder of the Woods should be thinned from below with some TSI removal of mature trees, leaving crop trees with room to grow. "Crop trees" are defined here as those the owner wishes to keep, some for aesthetic reasons, some for wildlife (including bees), and some for potential future harvest. The woods will be marked for a timber sale, with the aim of reducing total basal area to approximately 85 ft$^2$ per acre. All hemlock, white pine, healthy white oak, paper birch, and most sugar maple will be left. Approximately 80% of trees removed will be red maple. Remainder will be oaks that are crowding trees with higher crop value, or ash.

During logging, trees on the slope will be cable skidded to the ridge to keep equipment off the slope. Every reasonable effort will be made to minimize damage to residual trees. Logging must be done under snow-on conditions during the months of December through mid-March.

The Woods should be examined approximately 10 years after logging is completed, although a second timber harvest may not be needed for 15 years. The Woods should be checked annually for evidence of invasive species and oak wilt. Invasives should be killed with herbicide, or pulled immediately. Diseased trees should be removed for firewood during the winter.

Prepared by:  Clarence Paine, Consulting Forester
                Tuscarora, Wisconsin
                cpaine@trees.com
                897-555-1101

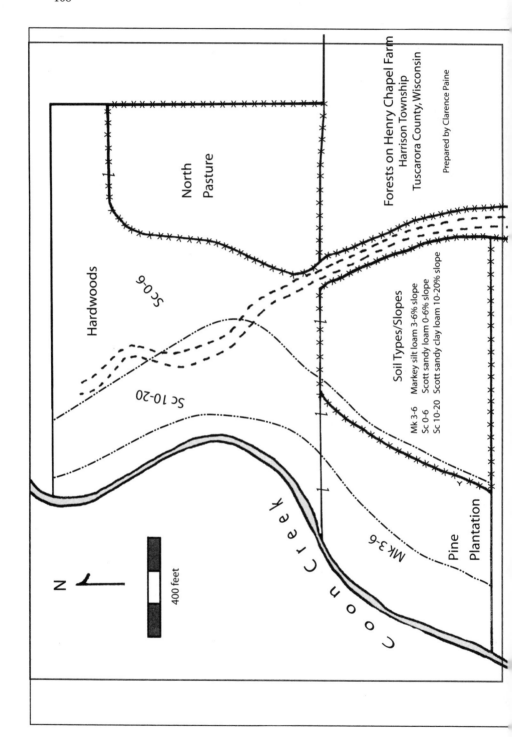

Forests on Henry Chapel Farm
Harrison Township
Tuscarora County, Wisconsin

Prepared by Clarence Paine

North Pasture

Hardwoods

Sc 0-6

Sc 10-20

Coon Creek

Mk 3-6

Pine Plantation

Soil Types/Slopes

Mk 3-6    Markey silt loam 3-6% slope
Sc 0-6    Scott sandy loam 0-6% slope
Sc 10-20  Scott sandy clay loam 10-20% slope

N

400 feet

# APPENDIX 10
## REQUEST FOR BIDS

### D R A F T

Henry Chapel and Homer Miller Farms

Harrison Township
Tuscarora County, Wisconsin

Two tracts of mature, mixed-hardwood timber, one 27 acres and the other 31 acres, are marked for timber stand improvement thinning. A third tract, 12 acres of unthinned red pine, is located adjacent to the 27 acres of hardwoods, and requires row thinning. The properties are located approximately three miles apart. Bids on either or both tracts will be considered, although preference will be given to bids that include both. A separate bid for the pine thinning is required, but preference will be given to the buyer that receives the winning bid for the hardwoods. The owners reserve the right to reject any or all bids and will be influenced by the professional reputation of the logger. References are required.

Purchaser must be certified in Wisconsin Best Management Practices (BMPs) through training in a FISTA coordinated BMP workshop.

If you wish to visit either or both tracts, please call the owners to arrange a time:
Henry Chapel (222-555-8888) or Homer Miller (222-555-9999)

Bids must be received, with three references of former clients, no later than 12:00 noon, August 1. Owners may choose to consider a late bid, but are under no obligation to do so.

Felling and skidding will be restricted to frozen-soil or snow-on conditions and may be shut-down if ground thaws before harvesting is completed. The successful buyer will have two years from the date of signing to complete the contract.

Mail bids to:  Charles Paine, Consulting Forester
Box 999, Tuscarora, Wisconsin 55555

Descriptions

Henry Chapel Tract (27 acres) located on Coon Creek Road (see map).
Approximately 10 acres of the hardwoods are on a moderately steep hill
that must be cable-skidded to the ridge. The remaining acreage is level
to gently rolling and can easily be worked with any type of equipment,
including a feller-buncher. A forwarder should be used to move wood
to the adjacent yard. All pulpwood is to be salvaged from tops. Only
marked trees are to be cut. There is truck access to the yard where
timber can be stacked for hauling. The pine plantation is immediately
adjacent to the hardwoods and will use the same yard. The plantation is
nearly level with easy access throughout.

Approximate volumes (Scribner Decimal C Log Rule):

> Red maple...........................112 MBF (thousand board feet)
> White ash........................... 14 MBF
> White oak........................... 5 MBF
> Red oak...............................7 MBF
> Black and pin oak.................8 MBF

Mixed hardwood pulp ( 4 inch min., proportioned approx. as
above)......225 cords.
Red pine pulp (3 inch min.).................................................150 cords

Homer Miller Tract (31 acres) located on Skunk Hollow Road (see map).
Entire tract is rolling but can be worked with any type of equipment,
although there are scattered large rocks that must be avoided. A
forwarder should be used to move wood to the adjacent yard. All
pulpwood must be salvaged from tops. Only marked trees are to be cut.
There is truck access to the yard.

Approximate volumes (Scribner Decimal C Log Rule):

> Red maple bolts..................123 MBF
> Aspen................................. 22 MBF
> White and green ash........... 17 MBF

Mixed hardwood pulp (4 inch min., proportioned approx. as
above).....250 cords

# APPENDIX 11
# TIMBER SALE CONTRACT

This example is based on a contract developed by Wisconsin Department of Natural Resources, University of Wisconsin Extension, and Wisconsin Woodland Owners (WWOA) in compliance with Wisconsin state laws and policies. Laws and policies may vary for other states, so check with the natural resource agency of your state, or your consulting forester.

This contract is entered into by and between Henry Chapel (Seller) and Greenwood Lumber, Ltd. (Purchaser) for the purpose of selling timber of the Seller. The Seller sells and the Purchaser agrees to purchase, cut and remove only those trees (timber) specifically marked by the Seller for cutting on the "sale area" which is identified and attached to this Contract.

The provisions of this contract and all authority for use of the Seller's property for the cutting of timber (which includes felling, bucking, skidding, loading and hauling) are mutually agreed upon by the Seller and Purchaser and subject to the following terms and conditions:

SAMPLE TIMBER SALE CONTRACT
This Contract is entered into by and between _____
_____(Seller), and

_____
(Purchaser). Contact information is listed in par. 53 of this agreement.
The Seller hereby authorizes the Purchaser to enter upon the following described lands (the Premises) for purposes of cutting and removing timber marked or otherwise designated by the Seller:
County: _____ Town Name: _____

_____
Town: __ N; Range __ ; Section _____; Legal Description(s)

_____
Town: __ N; Range __ ; Section _____; Legal Description(s)

_____
Those Premises are further described on the map(s) or diagram(s) attached to and made a part of this Contract.

FOR AND IN CONSIDERATION of the following terms and conditions the Seller and the Purchaser mutually agree:

CONTRACTING PARTIES

## 1. CONTRACTING PARTIES

a. Seller and Purchaser. In this Contract, the Seller and the Purchaser include their respective officers, employees, agents, directors, partners, representatives, successors, heirs and members.

b. Purchaser Ceases to Exist. If the Purchaser ceases to exist, in fact or by law, the Seller may terminate this Contract without waiving any remedies available to it and take all action necessary to assure its performance.

c. Subcontracting. This Contract or work under it may not be assigned or subcontracted in part or in whole without prior written approval from the Seller and may be changed or amended only in writing. The Purchaser agrees to notify the surety, if any, of any such change or amendment.

ENTIRE CONTRACT AND ATTACHMENTS

## 2. ENTIRE CONTRACT. This Contract, together with specifications in the request for bids as well as reference to parts and attachments, shall constitute the entire agreement and any previous communications or agreements pertaining to this Contract are hereby superseded. Any amendments to this Contract shall be in writing, signed and dated by both parties.

3. ATTACHMENTS. Any and all attachments to this Contract shall be made a part of this Contract and be fully complied with, including:

a. Map(s) or Diagram(s) of Sale Area;

b. Payment Schedule and Conditions of Payment;

c. Other: _____

_____

CONTRACT PERFORMANCE, PERIOD, EXTENSIONS AND TERMINATION

## 4. PERFORMANCE

a. Commencement. Cutting and removal of timber in conformance with this Contract may commence and continue only after the signing of this Contract by both parties and only after submission and maintenance of all bonds, certificates or statements required under it.

b. Contract Oversight. Cutting and removal of timber purchased under this Contract shall be conducted in conformance with this Contract and in a good and workmanlike manner with reasonable diligence to assure completion of all performance within the Contract period specified in par. 5. The Purchaser shall notify the Seller or the Seller's Agent 36-48 hours prior to commencing harvest of the timber designated herein and upon completion of the cutting. In the event that the harvest is temporarily discontinued for more than one week, the Purchaser agrees to notify the Seller or the Seller's Agent _____ (Agent's name) both upon discontinuance and resumption of harvest. Notification under this paragraph may be made by telephone to _____ (phone number). The Seller or the Seller's Agent may require an onsite meeting before commencement of harvesting.

c. Inspection. The Seller retains the right of ingress and egress to and on the sale area and may inspect the sale area and trucks hauling forest products from or traveling on the sale area at any time. If the inspection reveals any violations of this Contract the Seller shall promptly notice the Purchaser. Upon notice from the Seller, the Purchaser shall promptly take measures to remedy the violation.

d. Access. The Purchaser has no access or privilege to go upon the Seller's property other than to comply with this Contract and may not authorize access or use to others except for the sole purpose of performing this Contract.

Where options are listed with "OR", strike the option(s) that does not apply.

[Developed by the Wisconsin Dept. of Natural Resources, Wisconsin Woodland Owners Assoc. and Univ. of Wisconsin-Extension]


## 5. CONTRACT PERIOD

a. All work under this Contract shall be completed between the signing of the Contract by both Parties and _____ (Contract ending date), FOR TIME IS OF THE ESSENCE. Contract amendments or extensions may not be relied upon by the Purchaser for the purpose of completing performance under this Contract.

b. The Seller may temporarily suspend operations under this Contract due to excessive property damage, wet conditions or at other reasonable times upon notice to the Purchaser or other persons operating on the sale area under this Contract with subsequent equitable adjustment of this Contract as mutually agreed upon by the parties.

6. CONTRACT EXTENSIONS. If extensions of this Contract are deemed reasonable by the Seller, the stumpage price agreed upon herein shall be adjusted as follows:

a. First six-month extension: 0% increase

b. Second six-month extension: 5% increase

c. Additional six-month extensions: 10% increase

d. Other applicable charges or fees: _____

7. TERMINATION. The Seller may terminate this Contract by oral or written notice to the Purchaser upon its breach. Upon such notice, the Purchaser shall cease all operations on and immediately leave, and not return to, the Seller's property unless otherwise provided by the Seller.

## DOWNPAYMENT, BOND, REMEDIES AND DAMAGES

8. DOWNPAYMENT. The Purchaser has given the Seller a down payment in the form of cash, a certified check, or other form acceptable to the Seller in the amount of $_____ [if none, enter "zero"] to commit to completion of the timber sale in a timely manner as specified in the Contract.

9. BOND.

a. A performance bond in the Seller's favor in the amount of $_____ , in cash, by surety bond, or in any other form accepted by the Seller, shall be submitted by the Purchaser no later than _____ to be retained by the Seller to assure full and complete performance of the Contract by the Purchaser to the Seller's satisfaction. Failure to submit the bond shall be considered a breach of this Contract and subject the Purchaser to liability for damages. The Purchaser agrees that the bond shall be forfeited to the Seller as liquidated damages upon the Seller's determination that a condition or term of this Contract has been breached by the Purchaser, unless the Seller chooses and can reasonably determine the actual damages suffered as a result of the breach of the Contract. Damages assessed under this Contract are the responsibility of the Purchaser and may be deducted from this performance bond and otherwise collected by the Seller.

b. The Purchaser agrees that the performance bond may be retained by the Seller until all performance under this Contract has been completed to the Seller's satisfaction and the Seller determines the performance has been so completed. If the Seller determines the performance has not been completed satisfactorily and in conformance with this Contract, the performance bond may be retained by the Seller until the Seller can determine damages caused by the lack of performance. Only in the event the Purchaser provides written notice of sale completion to the Seller shall the Seller have sixty (60) days to determine that performance has been completed as required under this Contract

10. REMEDIES.

a. If timber or other forest products not specifically described in this Contract or designated by the Seller for cutting are cut, unreasonably damaged or removed by the Purchaser, the Seller may pursue any and all remedies for the unlawful use of the Seller's property and the cutting, unreasonable damage or removal of property without consent, including the seeking of criminal or civil charges for theft, timber theft or criminal damage to property, in addition to any Contract remedies for breach.

b. If the Seller or Purchaser seeks damages for breach of this Contract through court proceedings, and if either party prevails in such proceedings, in whole or in part, then the non-prevailing party agrees to pay all of the prevailing party's actual and reasonable expenses, including attorneys and expert witness fees.

c. The Seller agrees to mitigate the damages for breach by offering the timber for resale if it determines the timber is saleable based upon its volume or quality.

d. The Seller may, when it deems it reasonable and in the best interest of the Seller, allow the Purchaser to continue performance under the Contract and the Purchaser shall pay as liquidated damages double the mill value as determined by the Seller for the timber or other forest products cut, removed or damaged without authorization under or in violation of this Contract. The Seller's permission to continue cutting shall not be considered a waiver of breach nor prevent it from considering such breach for purposes of asserting any other remedies available to it. It is agreed that the double mill scale sum is a reasonable estimate of the probable damages suffered by the Seller and shall not be construed as or held to be in the nature of a penalty.

["Reasonable" in this contract is defined as fair, proper, just, moderate, and suitable under the circumstances, not arbitrary or capricious.]

11. DAMAGES. The damages to be paid to the Seller upon the Purchaser's failure to perform this Contract include, but are not limited to:

a. The difference between the Purchaser's bid value of timber not cut and removed under this Contract and the value returned to the Purchaser. The Seller agrees to mitigate the damages for breach by offering the timber for resale within 12 months if the Seller determines the timber is salable based upon its volume or quality.

b. Triple average stumpage rate established in NR 46.30, Wisconsin Administrative Rules, for timber cut, removed or unreasonably damaged without authorization under or in violation of this Contract. The Seller's decision to assess triple damages as provided here and to allow the Purchaser to continue performance under this contract shall not be construed as a waiver of other contract performance requirements.

c. All costs of sale area cleanup or completion of performance not completed by the Purchaser.

d. All costs of resale of timber not cut and removed as required under this Contract.

e. The Purchaser agrees that if the timber identified in this Contract for cutting is to be resold due to a breach of this Contract, the Seller is not obligated to give oral or written notice to the Purchaser of the resale.

f. Additional damage provisions:

_____

PRODUCTS TO BE REMOVED

12. No forest products may be removed from the Premises until the Purchaser pays for the products or guarantees payment for the products to the satisfaction of the Seller.

13. Title to stumpage and any forest products cut under this Contract shall remain with the Seller until payment is received. Title to stumpage and cut products that are not cut and removed before the end of the Contract period, even though paid for, shall revert to the Seller, and the Seller shall be under no obligation to return payments to the Purchaser.

14. During the period of this Contract, the Purchaser is authorized and shall cut, remove and pay for the timber or forest products marked or designated as follows:

_____

_____

_____

_____

## SALE TYPE, SCALING, HAULING AND PAYMENTS

15. SALE TYPE [select one of the following three choices and strike the others]

LUMP SUM SALE:

The Purchaser agrees to pay Seller an amount of $_____, to be paid in full prior to the commencement of timber cutting, based on the volume estimates and unit values in Par. 17 Timber Products Table. The Seller is not obligated to return the payment or any portion of it in the event the Purchaser fails to remove all timber or forest products authorized for removal.

OR

SCALED PRODUCTS SALE:

FLAT RATE METHOD. The payment as established by the Price per Unit in Par. 17 shall be based on sawtimber, cordwood, or piece product volume as measured by product dimensions. The price paid per board feet, cord or piece is a flat rate regardless of the quality, final destination or use of the cut product. Hardwood less than 10.6 inches in diameter at the small end of the log, inside the bark (d.i.b.), shall be measured as cordwood and 10.6 inches or greater d.i.b. as sawtimber. For conifers, the division between cordwood and sawtimber is 9.6 inches d.i.b. Sawtimber with 50% or more cull shall be measured as cordwood. The volume shall be measured by _____ (name), an agent of the Seller / the Purchaser / the primary processing facility (the Mill or its agent) to whom the Purchaser delivers the product and to whom the cut product is sold [strike the choices that do not apply].

OR

SCALED PRODUCTS SALE:

GRADED PRODUCT METHOD. The payment as established by the Price per Unit in Par. 17 shall be based on the volume of graded products including fuel wood, pulpwood, sawbolts, sawtimber by grade, veneer by grade and piece products (such as posts and utility poles) by grade. In addition to product dimension, the price paid depends upon the quality or intended use of the cut product or type of processing facility the cut product is destined. The volume and grade shall be determined by __ _____(name), an agent of the Seller / the Purchaser / the primary processing facility (the Mill or its agent) to whom the Purchaser delivers the product and to whom the cut product is sold [strike the choices that do not apply].

Lump sum and scaled products-flat rate methods are the most commonly accepted sale types. Landowners may have difficulty in finding purchasers willing to enter into graded product method sales, which are more difficult to administer.

[For example, cordwood delivered to a paper mill would be paid for as pulpwood. Cordwood delivered to a sawmill would be paid for as sawbolts or sawlogs.]

16. HAULING PROCEDURE5 AND PAYMENT SCHEDULE FOR SCALED SALES [select one of the following two choices and strike the other]

ON SITE SCALE. No products may be hauled from the Seller's property until scaled and paid for or payment has been arranged to the Seller's satisfaction in writing. Removing products otherwise shall be a violation of this Contract and considered theft.

OR

MILL SCALE. The Purchaser shall keep a record of each load removed and its destination. Addresses of the Mills where wood products are to be delivered shall be given to the Seller before cutting begins. The Purchaser shall provide Mills with the Seller's name and address for each load and request Mills to provide copies of the mill scale slips to the Seller within ___ days of receipt of the wood products. Failure to keep a record of any load and its destination shall be a violation of this Contract and considered theft. Payments shall be made according to the following schedule [pick one of the following three choices and strike the others]:

The Purchaser shall pay the Seller for the products delivered to the Mill, as measured on the mill scale slip, within ____ days of delivery. The Purchaser shall include copies of the mill scale slips with payments.

OR

Payment to the Seller shall be made in advance of hauling, with the value of the measured volume on the mill scale slips deducted from the Purchasers stumpage payment balance. The Seller agrees that advance stumpage payments shall not be used for any purpose other than the stumpage account and that any excess payments shall be returned to the Purchaser within 60 days after the last load is hauled from the Seller's property.

OR

The Mill shall make payments for delivered products directly to the Seller within ____ days of delivery by the Purchaser. Copies of the mill scale slips shall be included with payments to the Seller.

17. TIMBER PRODUCTS TABLE

The Purchaser agrees to pay the Seller the unit price for the volume of product by species that is harvested. In the case of lump

sum sales, the unit prices shall be used for sale add-ons or calculation of damages.

Species to be Harvested

Product (Sawtimber, Cordwood, Posts, Poles, Biomass, etc.)

Estimated Volume

Price per Unit (MBF, Cord, Piece, ton, etc.)

Total Value of Estimated Volume

Total Estimated Value:

18. Sawtimber volumes shall be determined by the Scribner Decimal C system (required for land enrolled under the Managed Forest Law or Forest Crop Law programs in Wisconsin).

19. Cord means 128 cubic feet of wood, air and bark assuming careful piling. Peeled cordwood shall be converted to standard cords using the Wisconsin DNR conversion specifications published in chapter NR 46.30 (1) (d), Wisconsin Administrative Code.

20. For Products measured by weight but paid for by cord the weights shall be converted to standard cords using one of the following

a. the Wisconsin DNR conversion specifications published in chapter NR 46.30 (1) (g)

b. the following weight conversions agreed to by the Seller and the Purchaser

species weight/cord species weight/cord

_____ _____ _____

_____ _____ _____

_____ _____

21. The volumes of timber indicated in this Contract or other appraisal or cruise documents of the Seller are estimates. The Seller gives no warranty or guarantee respecting the quantity, quality or volume of marked or otherwise designated timber or forest products on the sale

area.

[Information about an additional "Ticket System" for log hauling is also available from DNR, but is seldom used on private lands.
"MBF" means "thousand board feet"
Mills may measure cordwood with a 4" trim allowance, resulting in 133 cubic feet.
Proposed weight conversions should be included in the timber sale prospectus.]

## UTILIZATION AND OPERATIONS

22. STUMP HEIGHT; TOPS. Tree stumps shall be cut as close to the ground as practical, otherwise maximum stump height shall not exceed stump diameter; and for stumps ten or more inches in diameter, stumps shall not exceed ten inches in height. For sales including cordwood products, trees shall be utilized to a 4" minimum top diameter. Title to tops shall remain with the Seller and may not be utilized by the Purchaser, or at the Purchaser's direction, unless otherwise specified in this Contract.

23. WASTE. The Purchaser agrees to complete all operations and performance as described in this Contract without waste or nuisance on the sale area or any other property of the Seller or adjoining land used in conjunction with the harvest and use reasonable care not to damage trees not designated or marked for cutting. Young trees bent or held down by felled trees shall be promptly released.

24. ZONE COMPLETION. The Purchaser agrees to complete all operations on each portion of the sale area or each zone as designated on the sale area map, or other attachments or in the cutting requirements before beginning cutting in the next portion or zone, unless agreed to otherwise by the Seller.

25. DIGGERS HOTLINE. The Purchaser is responsible to contact the diggers hotline, or other informational sources performing similar services, prior to digging or conducting other activities on the property which may result in contact with utility or service lines or facilities.

26. ROADS, LANDINGS, MILL SITES, CAMPSITES, EROSION CONTROL, BEST MANAGEMENT PRACTICES (BMPs).

a. When not otherwise designated by the Seller, the location of roads, landings, mill sites and campsites on Seller's property are subject to advance approval and under the conditions established by the Seller. All restoration, cleanup or repair of roads, bridges, fences, gates, landings, mill sites and campsites, or the cost of the cleanup, if not completed by the Purchaser to the reasonable satisfaction of the Seller, is the responsibility of the Purchaser.

b. Logging debris accumulated at landing areas shall be scattered within the sale area to the reasonable satisfaction of the Seller.

c. Berms constructed on the Seller's property shall be leveled to restore the area to the Seller's satisfaction unless they are constructed at the direction of the Seller under sub d.

d.

Roads and landings shall be graded or closed upon the request of and to the Seller's satisfaction upon completion or termination of this Contract.

e. Other restoration requirements (e.g., seeding, gravel, rutting, culvert removal, etc.):

_____

_____

f. The Purchaser agrees to comply with the Best Management Practices (BMP) guidelines as described in "Wisconsin's Forestry Best Management Practices for Water Quality" published by the Wisconsin Department of Natural Resources, publication FR-093. Identify BMPs of particular concern:

_____

_____   _____

_____

_____

g. The Purchaser agrees to take precautions to prevent the spread of invasive species as described in Wisconsin Department of Natural Resources' invasive species guidelines. Identify species and actions of particular concern:

_____

_____   _____

_____

_____

## 27. SOIL DISTURBANCE AND RUTTING

a. The Purchaser agrees to take all steps and precautions to avoid and minimize soil disturbances, such as soil compaction and rutting. If soil disturbances occur, the Purchaser agrees to work cooperatively to mitigate and repair any and all instances of soil disturbance.

b. Excessive soil disturbance (as defined in Table 1) shall not be permitted. Purchaser agrees to contact Seller in the event of an excessive soil disturbance.

Table 1. Thresholds for soil disturbances.

Timber Sale Infrastructure

Soil disturbances are excessive if:

Roads, Landings, Skid Trails, and General Harvest Area

A gully or rut is 6 inches deep or more and is resulting in channelized flow to a wetland, stream, or lake.

Roads, Landings, and Primary Skid Trails

In a riparian management zone (RMZ) or wetland, a gully or rut is 6 inches deep or more and 100 feet long or more.

In an upland area (outside of RMZ), a gully or rut is 10 inches deep or more and 66 feet long or more.

Secondary Skid Trails and General Harvest Area

A gully or rut is 6 inches deep or more and 100 feet long or more.

Note: The depth is to be measured from the original soil surface to the bottom of the depression. If individual lug depressions are visible, the depth would be measured to the lesser of the two depths (the "top" of the lug). The length is measured from the start of the "too deep" section to the end of the "too deep" section. Measurements are not cumulative.

c. Prior to sale completion the Purchaser shall mitigate and repair soil disturbances to the Seller's satisfaction.

d. Other restoration requirements (e.g. repair of soil disturbance or rutting on recreational trails used for skidding):

(1)

_____

_____

(2)

28. OTHER APPROVALS. Logging roads that intersect town, county or state roads or highways must have the intersections approved by the proper authorities prior to construction and cleared of all unsightly debris at the time of construction. The Purchaser agrees to apply for and obtain all approvals. The Purchaser also agrees to fully comply with all terms and conditions of intersection approvals.

29. SURVEY MONUMENTS. The Purchaser agrees to comply with s. 59.635, Wis. Stats., regarding perpetuation of landmarks and pay for the cost of repair or replacement of property or land survey monuments or accessories which are removed, destroyed or made inaccessible.

30. FOREST FIRE PREVENTION. The Purchaser agrees to take reasonable precautions to prevent the starting and spreading of fires. Those precautions include, but are not limited to:

a. A minimum of one fully charged 5 pound or larger ABC fire extinguisher with a flexible spout shall be carried on each off-road logging vehicle.

b. All chainsaws and all non-turbocharged off-road logging equipment used in the operation shall be equipped with spark arrestors that have been approved by the U.S. Forest Service. Such arrestors may not be altered in any manner or removed and shall be properly maintained.

c. If a fire occurs, the Purchaser agrees to promptly report the fire and cooperate in the control and suppression of the fire.

d. The Purchaser shall comply with requests regarding forest fire prevention and suppression made by the Seller and take all reasonable precautions to prevent, suppress and report forest fires. Those requests may include ceasing or modifying operations.

e. The Purchaser shall be responsible for damage and forest fire suppression costs, including that provided in ss. 26.14 and 26.21, Wis. Stats., caused by their operation under this Contract.

f. Other:

31. SLASH REMOVAL. Slash as defined in s. 26.12, Wis. Stats., shall be disposed of as follows:

a. Slash falling in any lake or stream, in a right-of-way or on land of an adjoining landowner shall be immediately removed from the waters, right-of-way or adjoining land. Tops from felled trees may not be left hanging in standing trees. All trees shall be completely felled and not left leaning or hanging in other trees.

b. Other:

_____

_____

## 32. CLEANUP AND USE OF SALE AREA.

a. The Purchaser shall remove equipment, tools, solid waste and trash remaining on the sale area or Seller's property or adjoining land used in conjunction with the harvest upon completion of performance under this Contract, termination of this Contract due to breach by the Purchaser or when requested by the Seller.

b. No residence, dwelling, permanent structure, or improvement may be established or constructed on the sale area or other property of the Seller.

33. HAZARDOUS MATERIALS. The Purchaser agrees to properly use and dispose of all petroleum and hazardous products, including but not limited to oil, oil filters, grease cartridges, hydraulic fuel and diesel fuel. Any on-site spillage must be properly reported, removed and cleaned up by the Purchaser in accordance with applicable statutes and rules of the State of Wisconsin.

34. ADDITIONAL UTILIZATION AND OPERATION REQUIREMENTS AND INSTRUCTIONS:

a. Between April 15 and August 15 all pine products must be removed from the site within two weeks, regardless of when they were harvested.

b. Oak wilt prevention: where oak trees are present, no cutting is allowed between _____ and _____.

c. No trees or products over 16 feet in length may be skidded within the cutting area without written permission of the Seller.

d. Other (If none, state None.)

_____

_____

_____

_____

_____

_____

## NOTICE OF INTENT TO CUT AND COMPLIANCE WITH LAWS

35. SECTION 77 NOTICE AND REPORT. The Seller / Purchaser [select one] shall file required cutting notices and cutting reports to the responsible DNR forester for lands that are under the Forest Crop Law and Managed Forest Law programs.

36. SECTION 26 NOTICE. The Seller / Purchaser [select one] shall file a declaration annually with the county clerk in any manner acceptable to the county of his or her intentions to cut forest products pursuant to section 26.03, Statutes, and comply with all other notice requirements, laws and ordinances with respect to work under this Contract.

37. OTHER PERMITS. The Seller and Purchaser shall work together on acquiring other necessary permits (such as wetland or stream crossing permits).

38. APPLICABLE LAW. This Contract shall be governed by the laws of the State of Wisconsin. The Purchaser shall at all times comply with all federal, state, and local laws, ordinances and regulations in effect during the Contract period.

## TITLE, BOUNDARY LINES AND ACCESS

39. TITLE. The Seller warrants that the Seller has clear and unencumbered title to the stumpage subject to this Contract.

40. BOUNDARY LINES. The Seller guarantees to have the boundaries marked with paint or other suitable means before any timber is harvested.

41. ACCESS. The Seller agrees to secure entry and right-of-way to the Purchaser on and across the area covered by this Contract, including access via land owned by a third-party if necessary.

## LIABILITY AND INSURANCE

42. The Purchaser agrees to protect, indemnify and save harmless the Seller and the Seller's employees and agents from and against all causes of action, claims, demands, suits, liability or expense by reason of loss or damage to any property or bodily injury to any person, including death, as a direct or indirect result of timbering operations under this Contract or in connection with any action or omission of the Purchaser, who shall defend the Seller in any cause of action or claim.

43. Unless the Purchaser is exempted by the Seller from this coverage requirement as an independent contractor, as defined in s. 102.07(8)(b),

Stats., and as determined by the Seller based on an affidavit submitted to it, the Purchaser agrees to elect to maintain worker's compensation insurance coverage for the cutting operation under this Contract and any and all employees engaged in cutting on the Seller's land during the period of this Contract regardless of any exemptions from coverage under chapter 102, Wis. Stats. The Purchaser must provide an original certificate of insurance naming the Seller as a certificate holder so the insurance carrier can notify the Seller should the insurance expire.

44. The Purchaser agrees to furnish the Seller with a certificate of public liability insurance covering the period of logging operations on the Seller's property for:

a. $1,000,000 single limit liability for personal injury or $1,000,000 bodily injury per person and $1,000,000 per occurrence; and

b. $100,000 property damage.

45. The Purchaser shall notify the Seller in writing, immediately upon any change in or cancellation of insurance coverage required by this Contract.

46. The Purchaser is an independent contractor for all purposes including Worker's Compensation and is not an employee or agent of the Seller. The Seller agrees that the undersigned Purchaser, except as otherwise specifically provided herein, shall have the sole control of the method, hours worked, time and manner of any timber cutting to be performed hereunder. The Seller reserves the right only to inspect the job site for the sole purpose of insuring that the cutting is progressing in compliance with the cutting practices established under this Contract. The Seller takes no responsibility for supervision or direction of the performance of any of the harvesting to be performed by the undersigned Purchaser or its employees. The Seller further agrees to exercise no control over the selection and dismissal of the Purchaser's employees.

County cutting notices expire by law on December 31 and so must be renewed annually.

47. OSHA COMPLIANCE, DANGER TREES. The Purchaser is responsible to comply with, and assure compliance by all employees or subcontractors with, all Occupational Safety and Health Act (OSHA) requirements for the health and safety of Purchaser's employees, including provisions relating to danger trees. In addition, the Purchaser agrees to notify, and obtain agreement from, the Seller if the Purchaser intends to modify performance required under this Contract for the purpose of compliance with OSHA requirements. Not withstanding

OSHA regulations, the Purchaser agrees to apply appropriate safety precautions.

48. ACTS OF GOD. Neither party shall be liable for defaults or delays due to acts of god or the public enemy, acts or demands of any government or governmental agency, strikes, fires, flood, accidents or other unforeseeable causes beyond its control and not due to its fault or negligence. Each party shall notify the other in writing of the cause of such delay within five days after the beginning thereof. If such uncontrollable circumstances continue for 30 days and prevent either party from complying with the terms of this agreement, either party shall have the option of terminating upon ten days notice to the other.

## TRAINING (Recommended)

49. TRAINING REQUIREMENT. The Purchaser is responsible for ensuring that the actual logging contractor engaged in performance of this Contract holds a current logging safety training certificate issued by the Forest Industry Safety & Training Alliance (FISTA) or equivalent safety training acceptable to the seller. Purchaser agrees to provide documentation to Seller that training has been attained prior to initiating sale.

## FOREST CERTIFICATION (if applicable)

50. CERTIFICATION STANDARD AND CERTIFICATE . The land management area encompassed by this timber sale is certified to the following forest certification standards (mark as applicable and provide valid certificate numbers):

___ American Tree Farm System (ATFS) Certificate # ___ _____

___ Forest Stewardship Council (FSC) Certificate # ___ _____

___ Sustainable Forestry Initiative (SFI) Certificate # _____

___ _____ (Other Standard) Certificate #

_____

51. CHAIN OF CUSTODY. Forest certification chain of custody provided by the Seller under the preceding certificates ends at the stump, log landing or roadside.

52. APPROVED CUTTING NOTICE. In the event that land management area encompassed by this timber sale participates in the Wisconsin Managed Forest Law Certified Group, the Seller agrees to

provide the Purchaser with a copy of the Wisconsin DNR approved Cutting Notice (DNR Form 2450-32).

CONTACT INFORMATION

53. CONTACT INFORMATION:

(Note: Separate from this form, the Seller and Purchaser are encouraged to provide one another with their Social Security Number or Federal Employer ID Number, needed to file tax returns or other financial documents.)

Seller: _____

Address: _____

_____ _____

_____

Phone: _____

Cellular Phone: _____

Purchaser:

Name _____

Address: _____

_____ _____

_____

Phone: _____

Cellular Phone: _____

We have read and understand the entire Contract comprised of _____ pages.

SELLER

Date _____ by _____

_____

PURCHASER

Date _____ by _____

_____

# APPENDIX 12
# TIMBER HARVESTING

1. Prepare and follow your management plan. Even if you are doing your own timber harvest, it is important to follow a management plan (see Forest Management Plan, Appendix 9). It is not possible to properly mark trees for a timber harvest unless your management goals and objectives are clearly defined. That is the primary purpose of a management plan.

2. Hiring a consulting forester. Most landowners should hire a consulting forester on a cash-for-service basis. Contracting on a commission basis tempts the forester to mark too many trees. Be suspicious of any consulting forester who prefers a percentage of stumpage sale for their services.

3. Marking trees for harvest. Except for clearing down wood, or cutting a diseased tree here and there, it is best to clearly mark the trees selected for harvest, even if you are doing your own felling. Use a durable paint, and place slash marks about head high on two sides of each tree to be cut. If a logger is going to do your felling, also place a paint mark near the ground to indicate that a tree was marked. After the tree has been removed, the mark on the stump verifies that the tree was selected for removal. Some woodland owners have enough knowledge and experience to mark trees themselves, although if they are to be sold, a forester may need to determine the volumes. If possible, spend the first few hours with the forester and ask about trees for which the decision to cut or leave is not clear. If you aren't satisfied with the answer, have the decision reversed and ask the forester to mark accordingly for the rest of the stand. The forester will determine timber volume for each species.

4. Get multiple bids from loggers and write an explicit contract. Some woodland owners have enough knowledge and experience to advertise, select a logger, and execute a contract. To avoid liability and workman's compensation insurance, never hire a logger to cut the wood for you to sell. Sell the timber as it stands. Even if you hire a consulting forester to set up the timber sale, work closely with them in the selection of the logger. If available, preference should be given to certified loggers. Getting references and taking to others who have sold timber to a logger are common-sense practices. There is no requirement to take the high bid. Most landowners are more interested in the visual quality and ecological health of the forest after harvest than they are in getting

the highest cash return.

5. If possible, be there when the saws are running. Few woodland owners can be on site the entire time the harvest is in progress. Recognize that timber harvesting is dangerous and most loggers will have far more experience and knowledge of the process than you. If you and your consulting forester are quite clear about your expectations, and you have hired a competent consultant, and you have a good contract, it is less critical that you be present during the harvest. It is common for consulting foresters to know the logger, but they should not be too cozy. Keep in mind that both are working for you. Your presence sends a good message to both.

6. Be assertive about clean-up and settling up. Treetops can be utilized for firewood, piled for wildlife, or lopped down to improve aesthetics. Whatever the contract requires, make sure it is done as logging proceeds. Forest roads should be repaired before the logging equipment leaves the site. Expect the wood to be hauled to the mill as soon as the private and public roads are stable. If the trees were sold on a volume basis, make sure you get all the scale slips from the mill purchasing the wood from the logger. The total volume should be reasonably close to the original estimate. Share any and all concerns with your consulting forester.

7. Remember the IRS. Timber sales are commonly treated as capital gains. This works to your advantage since capital gains are taxed at a lower rate than ordinary income. Capital gains, however, require you to know what your timber was worth when you purchased or inherited it (basis). If you don't have long-term records, you will need to have your consulting forester use growth-rate models and historical timber prices to determine your basis. Consult a tax advisor familiar with forestry business practices.

# APPENDIX 13
# MAPLE SYRUP

A great benefit of managing a woodlot that contains maples is the opportunity to make maple syrup. Tapping maples and boiling syrup is one of the first projects that can be done in the spring, nearly always before all the snow is gone and the ground has dried enough. Depending on the scale, making maple syrup can be demanding of both time and energy, so it usually is done only by those who find pleasure in working outdoors, often under inclement weather conditions.

All our native maple species are suitable for tapping, even box-elder. Sugar maple, of course, is the traditional species, and on average, has a slightly higher percent sugar content. Flavor of the syrup, however, is quite similar from other species, but longer boiling is required and syrup tends to be darker.

Trees should be tapped when daytime temperatures regularly get over 35 degrees and nighttime temperatures stay above the 20-degree range. Depending on location, this period falls in late February to early April. March is the primary period for sugaring.

Watch the long-range weather forecast and try to pick a time when favorable weather is predicted for the next week or ten days. Be sure to have equipment ready, including an outdoor or out-building place to do the boiling.

Equipment required:

1. Cordless drill or brace-and-bit with 7/16th sharp bit. (Have two bits if you are going to tap more than 30 trees.)
2. Spiles to insert in holes.
3. Buckets with lids, or plastic tubing to collect sap.
4. Tank for gathering or collecting sap. Clean five-gallon buckets can be used to carry sap to boiler in small operations.
5. Holding tank at boiler for accumulating sap.
6. Evaporation pan.
7. Sieve for straining sap
8. Skimmer
9. Finishing pan or kettle
10. Sterile jars for syrup.

Additionally, you may want a candy thermometer to determine the optimal time for bottling the syrup. Metal strainers and cheesecloth will be useful to remove any debris that will get into the sap. For commercial grade syrup, a filter is needed to remove sediment, although for personal use, the syrup can be decanted off leaving sediment in the bottom of the jar. Filters are also available if you want less "sugar sand."

When tapping, angle the hole slightly so that it will drain easily. This reduces risk of decay in old tap-holes. Holes should be 1.5 to 2 inches deep. Spiles are plastic, metal or wood. They can be twisted into the hole or tapped lightly with a mallet or the handle of a hammer. Buckets can be hung on the spile, and should be fitted with a lid to keep out rain, insects and debris.

When using plastic tubing, the sap will run by gravity flow into a central collection tank. If using buckets, they need to be emptied daily when conditions are good, and under ideal conditions, sap may need to be gathered twice a day. Sap will freeze in the buckets on cold nights, so it is best to pick it up late in the day. Straining the ice out concentrating the sugar

When boiling, filter 4-6 inches of sap into the evaporator and place a good fire in the boiler. A strainer will remove coarse debris, but filtering through a cheesecloth is necessary to remove fine debris that nearly always gets into buckets. As sap begins to boil, skim off foam that will form. Keep the fire going strong, and continue to add sap as the level in the boiler to maintain two to four inch depth. Depending on the year, your trees, and the species of maple, plan on boiling 35 to 45 gallons of sap for each gallon of syrup.

Continue boiling and adding sap for any reasonable time and volume you wish. With a modest evaporating pan and good fire, you can usually boil down 40 to 50 gallons in a 12-hour day. Few people try to finish syrup on the boiler because the risk of scorching is too great. Drain off the reduced sap when you can fit it into a finishing pan. Depending on the finishing pan, you may be able to take off two or three gallons at this point.

Finish the syrup on a stove with good heat control, such as a gas stove. If using a stainless kettle, you can reduce two gallons of unfinished syrup overnight on the lowest setting of the stove. This should be done outdoors or in an outbuilding. The moisture released from evaporation is a problem indoors unless you have a very good ventilation fan. Ideally, reduce the syrup until the boiling point is about 220 degrees, give or take a degree, on a candy thermometer. If you want thicker syrup, you can go higher. When done, turn off the stove, allow the syrup to set for a few minutes, then ladle it into sterile jars and seal. If filtering then keep the syrup as hot as possible and filter immediately. Syrup will keep indefinitely without refrigeration if sealed this way.

A layer of sediment will form in the bottom of jars unless the syrup if filtered before bottling. The sediment does not affect the flavor. It is rich in minerals, and can be used on toast or pancakes, or in cooking. Otherwise, decant the syrup when pouring from the jar.

# GLOSSARY

**all-aged stand** - a stand of trees of many sizes and ages, indicating re-generation over an extended time period.

**annual rings** - see growth ring.

**aspect** - direction a slope faces.

**basal area** - the total cross-sectional area of trees at breast height per unit area, usually expressed as square feet per acre in United States; an indication of the volume of trees per unit area.

**biodiversity** - the natural communities and species that are present in a defined area.

**blaze** - traditionally an ax mark on well positioned trees, now usually a paint mark on such trees; may also indicate a timber-sale boundary or an internal delineation between "cut" and "don't cut" areas.

**blowdown** - a tree that has been blown over by wind, either tipped-up or broken off; sometimes used to describe a forest where many trees have been blown down .

**board feet** - a measure of the volume of wood that can be cut from a log, estimated by one of several formulas from the diameter; a unit that is 1 inch thick, 12 inches wide and 12 inches long.

**bole** - the stem of a tree.

**breast height** - 4.5 feet above mean ground level, the conventional height at which the diameter of a tree is measured.

**browse** - coarse vegetation such as twigs consumed by animals such as deer or moose that tend to nibble as they move through a forest or meadow; the act of eating coarse woody vegetation.

**canopy** - the top of the forest where the crowns of dominant and co-dominant trees co-mingle.

**carrying capacity** - more commonly applied to wildlife or livestock, it is the maximum number of individuals that can be sustained in the habitat without degrading the habitat.

**clear-cut harvest** - a harvest in which all merchantable material is re-moved, and often remaining stems cut to the ground.

**co-dominant tree** - a tree whose crown shares the upper canopy with other co-dominant trees.

**cord** - a stack of wood that is 128 cubic feet (a pile 8 feet long, 4 feet high and 4 feet wide) often a measure by which pulpwood and bolts are sold.

**cordwood** - small diameter sticks, usually 3 to 10 inches in diameter, used for pulpwood, firewood, or chips.

**crop tree** - A tree that contributes to the goal of the land owner or manager, and would be favored during a timber stand improvement (tsi) harvest. A crop tree might have value for future timber, or for aesthetics, wildlife, or diversity. Why it would be valued depends on the goals of the landowner and how the tree relates to them.

**crown** - the uppermost living branches of a tree; what you would see looking down on the tree from above.

**cruise** - the process of surveying a forest, usually to estimate species and volumes of timber.

**deciduous** - plants, especially trees and shrubs, that lose all their leaves at the same time.

**diameter breast height (dbh)** - the diameter of a tree at 4.5 feet above mean ground level, used to calculate basal area, or volume of wood in a tree.

**diversity** - An ecological value based on the number and distribution of different species, communities, and even the genetic variation within species that make up a landscape.

**dominant tree** - a larger tree whose crown is above most other trees.

**ecosystem** - the total of all organisms and the non-living components of their habitat in a defined area.

**even-aged stand** - a stand of trees that are all about the same age and size, indicating that they were planted or regenerated at the same time and under similar conditions.

**exotic species** - a non-native species that may or may not be invasive.

**felling** - cutting trees.

**forest community** - all the organisms, including microorganisms, that interact in an area through predator-prey, competition, disease-host, parasite-host, and synergetic relationships.

**growth rings** - an annual layer of woody cells in the stem of a tree, indicating the radial growth that year.

**habitat** - the preferred site for a species, or the place where a species is usually found.

**high grading** - a practice of harvesting the biggest and most valuable trees; considered short-sighted because the next generation usually will produce less valuable trees.

**intolerant** - a species that grows poorly in the shade or in competition with other plants.

**invasive species** - A species of plant or animal, native or non-native, that tends to aggressively advance at the expense of other plants or animals, often leading to reduced diversity.

**live-crown ratio** - the ratio of the portion of the tree with live limbs to the total height of the tree.

**lump-sum sale** - sale of merchantable trees from a designated area as a lump-sum, as contrasted to a scaled sale in which the buyer pays according to the volume or weight of merchantable material removed.

**mast** - seeds and fruits, especially nuts, used as food by one or more species of wildlife.

**merchantable height** - the height or length of a bole (trunk) of a tree that can be marketed.

**mesic** - Intermediate drainage, neither particularly wet nor particularly dry.

**over-mature** - generally used as an economic term to indicate that growth of a tree or stand has slowed down to the point that financial yield is less than could be earned by harvesting and investing the money. Also used to characterize a stand that is nearing the normal end of life for the species.

**over-stocked** - basal area or tree density so great that growth is impaired.

**overstory** – the larger trees whose crowns are above smaller trees and scrubs.

**performance bond** - securities offered to the seller to insure that the logger does not default or to cover logging damages not allowed in the contract.

**precommercial treatment** - a silvicultural thinning practice in a stand that is too immature to yield any merchantable material.

**prism** - a ground glass that diffracts light and which can be calibrated to estimate basal area of a stand.

**prospectus** - a document which describes the volume, species, sizes, location, and other pertinent details of a prospective timber harvest, generally prepared to solicit bids.

**release** - a silvicultural practice in which some or all overstory trees are removed to provide more light and room for smaller trees.

**residual trees** - living trees remaining after a harvest.

**row thinning** - thinning of a plantation in which entire rows of trees are removed.

**scaled sale** - a timber sale in which the buyer pays for the measured (scaled) material as it is removed from the forest.

**sealed-bid** - bids are sealed until the opening date and time when all offers are examined together.

**selection harvest** - a harvest in which only certain trees are removed.

**silviculture** - the art and science of growing trees or managing a forest

**site index** - a measure of the ability of a site to grow trees of a particular species as indicated by height of dominant trees at a specified age, usually 25 or 50 years, depending on species.

**site preparation** - treatment of a site in preparation for seeding or planting.

**slash** - limbs and other debris left after a timber harvest.

**snag** - living or dead tree with heart-wood decay, often hollow or with cavities that are used by a variety of wildlife species.

**species** - an interbreeding population of organisms that look alike and have similar habitat requirements.

**stand** – a group of trees of the same or different species, often of similar ages, that can be managed as a unit.

**stick** - a piece of wood 100 inches long, the standard length for pulpwood.

**stumpage** - the value of standing timber in a defined area.

**suppressed** - trees whose growth is impaired as a result of being overtopped by other trees.

**sustained yield** - management in such a way that growth of the resource, on average, equals the harvest, in perpetuity.

**timber stand improvement** - a harvest in which less desirable trees are removed leaving better trees to continue to grow.

**tolerance** - the capacity of a plant to grow in competition with other plants, especially applied to the capacity of trees to grow in shade of other trees.

**tsi** - see "timber stand improvement."

**understory** – vegetation beneath the canopy of a forest, sometimes indicating only the smaller trees.

**uneven-aged stand** - a stand of trees of mixed sizes and ages, resulting from periodic reproduction over many years.

# Resources and Additional Information

1. Wisconsin DNR. 2006. 2006 Directory of Foresters. Wisconsin Department of Natural Resources, Division of Forestry, P.O. Box 7921, Madison, WI 53707

2. Hanson, Kirk. On-going. The Entrepreneurial Forester. A news bulletin for small woodland owners, focused primarily on the Northwest. kirg@nnrg.org

3. Wisconsin DNR. On-going. Forest Management Guidelines for Wisconsin. Extensive, and detailed guidelines for all aspects of forest management in Wisconsin (widely applicable to much of the Upper Midwest). http://dnr.wi.gov/forestry/Publications/Guidelines/ Also, available in CD from: Wisconsin DNR—Forestry Publications, P.O. Box 7921, Madison, WI 53707.

4. U.S. Forest Service. On-going. A Forest Landowners Guide to the Internet. This resource provides links to sources of forestry related information across the country, and includes about every topic pertinent to forestry, from recreation to hunting, estate planning, management, and much more. http://na.fs.fed.us/pubs/miscs/flg

5. Community Forestry Resource Center. On-going. CFRC promotes sustainable forest management through assisting private woodland owners with management and networking opportunities. They are especially interesting in helping those who wish to develop an association or cooperative or in becoming certified through the Forest Stewardship Council (FSC). Groups seeking help can contact CFRC at: 2105 First Avenue S., Minneapolis, MN 55404

Email: forestrycenter@iatp.org

6. Wisconsin Certified Master Logger. Members have passed a required training program and their work has been inspected and certified. If you are in need of a logger, and want to consider Master Loggers in your area, you can view the list at: http://www.wpla.org/master.html

7. forestry.guide@about.com Blog by Steve Nix that provides a wealth of forestry-related information, regularly updated. Applies primarily to Upper Midwest and Northeast, but much of the information is more generally applicable.

8.    http://dnr.wi.gov/forestry/Publications/Newsletters/forestrynotes. html_Forestry newsletters with information of interest to private woodland owners in Wisconsin.

9. www.forestryusa.com   Excellent source for information on most forestry-related topics, including state and regional resources.

# About the Authors

**Alan Haney** is an Emeritus Professor of Forestry at the University of Wisconsin-Stevens Point where he also served as Dean of the College of Natural Resources (1988-98). During his 36 years as a professor, Alan taught forest ecology, dendrology, silvics, and silviculture, among other subjects. His forestry education began as a child as he followed his grandfather through several hundred acres of mixed hardwoods that he owned and managed in southern Ohio. Later in his college career, Alan managed 700 acres of hardwood forests and pine plantations at Warren Wilson College in the southern Appalachians. After moving to Wisconsin, Alan purchased two properties in central Wisconsin that include a combined total of 120 acres of hardwood forests. Alan's most recent book (co-authored with Steven Apfelbaum) is *Restoring Health to Your Land*, published by Island Press (2010).

**Lowell Klessig,** Emeritus Professor of Human Dimensions of Natural Resource Management at the University of Wisconsin-Stevens Point, has been managing mixed hardwood and pine forests for 39 years. He owns 80 acres of woodlands in each of three counties in central and northern Wisconsin. He also operates a beef farm. Prior to retirement, Lowell was a UW-Extension Lakes Specialist and taught Integrated Resource Management. He concurrently served as Executive Director of the Wisconsin Rural Leadership Program, and developed the Wisconsin Woodland Leaders Institute and Wisconsin Master Woodlands Stewards Program.